# Civil Engineering Drawing

*Humber Bridge. Lifting the first road section.*
*(Photograph supplied by the New Civil Engineer)*

# Civil Engineering Drawing

**D. V. Jude**

Revised by **Robert B. Matkin** M.A., C.Eng.
*Recently Lecturer, Department of Civil Engineering*
*The City University, London*

**Second Edition**

**GRANADA**
London Toronto Sydney New York

Granada Publishing Limited – Technical Books Division
Frogmore, St Albans, Herts AL2 2NF
and
36 Golden Square, London W1R 4AH
515 Madison Avenue, New York, NY 10022, USA
117 York Street, Sydney, NSW 2000, Australia
100 Skyway Avenue, Rexdale, Ontario, Canada M9W 3A6
61 Beach Road, Auckland, New Zealand

First Edition copyright © 1971 by McGraw-Hill Publishing Company Limited
Second Edition copyright © 1983 by D. V. Jude and Robert B. Matkin

*British Library Cataloguing in Publication Data*

Jude, D. V.
   Civil engineering drawing.—2nd ed.
   1. Structural drawing.    2. Architectural drawing
   I. Title    II. Matkin, Robert B.
   604.2'4    T355

   ISBN 0 246 11752 4

First published in Great Britain 1971 by McGraw-Hill Publishing Company
Limited, Maidenhead, Berkshire, England.

Second edition published 1983 by Granada Publishing Limited

Typeset by V. & M. Graphics Ltd, Aylesbury, Bucks
Printed and bound in Great Britain by
William Clowes (Beccles) Limited, Beccles and London

Granada ®
Granada Publishing ®

# Contents

ILLUSTRATIONS

## PREFACE TO FIRST EDITION

The last quarter of the twentieth century will see more construction than ever before in the history of mankind. More people will require better accommodation, transport systems, and recreational facilities. As civil engineers, we are responsible for the basis of the environment that man has come to accept; we design and build his roads, docks, and airports; we provide him with water and remove his sewage; we also play a large part in providing him with gas and electricity. For this to be done more quickly, more efficiently, and more cheaply than in the past, there must be a constant interchange of ideas and precise information between all engineering disciplines and all nations.

It is here that engineering drawing comes into its own as the undisputed international language of the engineer. A language that must be acquired by the student of civil engineering as soon as possible.

The aim of this book is to teach some of the fundamentals of this language in a straight-forward way, for the civil engineering student has, in the past, lacked books dealing specifically with engineering drawing. There are many good books concerned with projection and geometry, as well as others incorporating 'engineering drawing' in the title, but no book known to the author has attempted to provide primarily for the needs of the civil engineer.

The content of all technological courses increases year by year and time must be saved somewhere. This can be done, to some extent, if all the student's exercises, including drawing, are concerned with civil engineering, so that he begins to see and think professionally from the start.

Although the later sections of this book, which discuss drawing in practice, may not affect the student immediately, they are intended to give him a background to the role of drawing in civil engineering and should help to explain why things are done in the way they are. It is hoped that the photographs of schemes and structures will play a part in conveying how exciting and challenging the field can be.

Several references are made in the text to the necessity of saving time, since skilled men's time is so expensive, and to the need to reduce errors and chances of ambiguity. To this end, the student should familiarize himself at an early stage with the appropriate British Standards, references to which are given in the text.

**Acknowledgements**

The sources of the photographs and the working drawings reproduced facsimile are included in their captions. While gratefully acknowledging permission to use this material, I should also like to thank many other individuals for so willingly giving their time in correspondence and discussion.

In addition, extracts from BS4: *1962, Part 1, Specification for Structural Steel Sections;* BS 308: *1964, Engineering Drawing Practice;* BS 1192: *1953, Drawing Office Practice for Architects and Builders;* and BS 3429: *1961, Specification for Sizes of Drawing Sheets* are reproduced by permission of the British Standards Institution, 2 Park Street, London, W1 from whom copies of the complete standards may be obtained.

D. V. Jude

## PREFACE TO SECOND EDITION

In the eleven years since the late Mr Jude prepared the book for publication, there has been a great change in the commercial preparation of drawings. Computerised draughting machines are now replacing many of the routine tasks formerly undertaken by draughtsmen and tracers.

New types of draughting equipment, compass, scales, pencil lead holders and drawing pens appear regularly, but fundamentally they perform the same tasks under the skilled hands of the operator.

There is no change however in the basics of engineering drawing, orthographic and pictorial projection, geometrics, developments and intersections, conics and the practice of drawing at the board. The only way to the understanding of drawings and to good draughtsmanship is to practise the art constantly, for art it is and one where practice, practice and more practice is the only way towards reaching near perfection.

For these reasons, the reader will find some sections have changed little, whilst others have undergone some major revision. It is hoped that this new edition will continue to fill the needs of those requiring a book devoted to the theory and practice of civil engineering drawing.

Robert B Matkin
1982

# Part One        Drawing

# Chapter 1        Equipment

*Model of the Thames Barrier as it will appear on completion. (Photograph supplied by the Greater London Council)*

## 1.1 THE MECHANICS OF ENGINEERING DRAWING

Engineering drawings are based upon a pair of axes, x and y, at right angles to each other, but not necessarily parallel to the edges of the drawing surface. The simplest way of providing these axes is by a square or parallel rule and set squares on a drawing board, Fig. 1.1.

It is convenient to have the most frequently used fixed angles on the set squares and two will be required with angles of 90°/45° and 90°/60°/30°.

The choice and quality of instruments is an individual one and generally gained through usage and experience, each person having likes and dislikes of any particular 'model'. The best advice that can be given is not to buy cheap goods but to choose your equipment with care, examining carefully the construction and quality and, rejecting anything which shows indifferent workmanship. (See, for example, that there are no rough edges to set squares or rules.) Drawing instruments, like most other things, offer better quality the more you pay. But quality, no matter how good, will not produce better quality drawings unless the person using them is professionally competent.

It is not advisable to start by purchasing sets of equipment, buying individual items means you can shop around to get the most suitable items from a varied selection of manufacturers.

Always remember one thing, drawing equipment is generally something you buy only once in your life, so obtain the quality of goods that will last.

## 1.2 DRAWING INSTRUMENTS AND OTHER EQUIPMENT

There are three main headings in this section:
(a) personal drawing equipment and its use
(b) materials on which drawings are made
(c) methods of supporting the drawing materials.

### (a) Personal drawing equipment

Some of the essential items of personal equipment that are required by a student comprise:
(a) set squares
(b) scale rule
(c) compass or beam compass
(d) springbow compass
(e) pencils
(f) eraser
(g) erasing shield
(h) sandpaper block
(j) protractor
(k) drawing board clips
(l) duster.

1.1 *Drawing board ready for use with paper held in place by clips.*

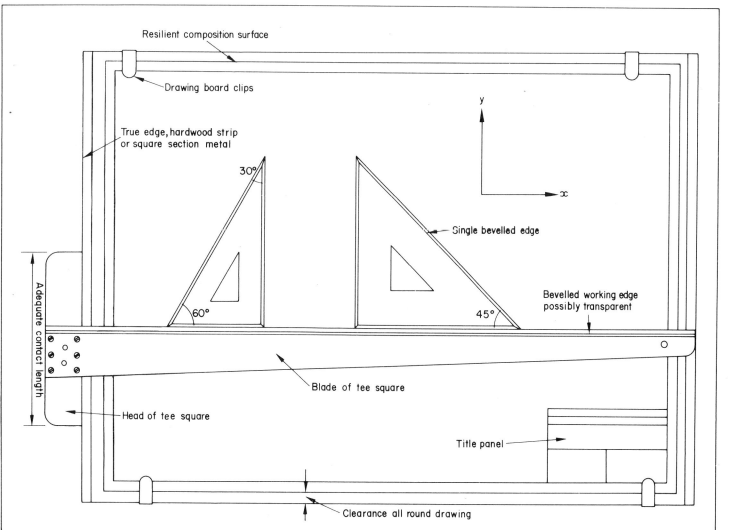

(As the letter i, especially as a capital, can be confused with the number one or the letter I particularly in freehand writing, it should not be used as a reference.)

A smaller list of equipment includes some items that will be found useful at a later stage:

(m) adjustable set square

(n) french curves and flexible curve

(o) pens.

A brief description of these items follows with some notes on their use.

**Set squares**. As the name implies these are squares with set or fixed angles. They are generally made of plastic and of two types, the 45° and 60°/30°. A reasonable size set square measures about 250 to 300 mm on the long side. It is advisable to have them with the edges bevelled on one face only. With the bevelled edge uppermost, accurate pencil work can be done, whilst ink can be used when the bevel is underneath. In this way there is little fear of blots or smudges.

The accuracy of the right angle can be checked as shown in Fig. 1.2 by swinging the set square from the dotted to the full-line position on a straight edge about the point C. A line drawn along the edge BC each time will indicate the double error. Fig. 1.3 shows how a perpendicular can be drawn using two set squares.

When moving set squares about the drawing always lift them before changing the position, otherwise dirt or dust on the drawing will cause smudges and give the drawing an untidy appearance.

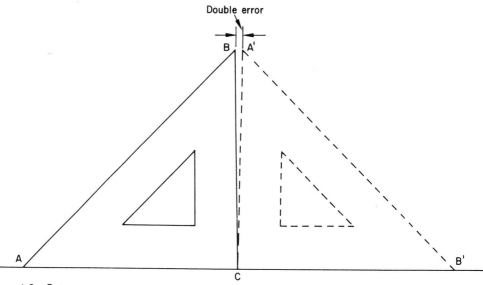

1.2  Set square error.

**Scale** (Fig. 1.4). The term scale in drawing can mean two things, it can be the scale of a drawing, see Chapter 3, or the instrument used to measure distances on a drawing.

There are several varieties of scale manufactured, but the most favoured are those with either an oval cross section (Fig. 1.4 (a)) or of triangular construction (Fig. 1.4 (b)). Each side of the scale carries a different scale ratio and these vary according to the type of work they are to be used for. They should have plastic edges.

On an oval scale four different scale ratios can be engraved whilst on the triangular model this goes up to six scale ratios, even these are increased on some models by doubling up the number of scales per edge, i.e. 1:10 and 1:100

being engraved together. The scales suitable for the student are 1:2.5, 1:5, 1:10, 1:20.

Never use the scale for ruling lines or slitting paper. Always use the right scale ratio and do not convert from a different ratio. Never use the scale to set compass radii or divider distances, always mark the required distance on a piece of paper and use these marks for the setting.

**Compass or beam compass** (Fig. 1.5). These are used to draw circles of radii over about 40 mm, the beam compass with its extension bar can draw much larger circles. The compass point is usually reversible, one point being shouldered to prevent it making a large hole in the paper should a number of circles have to be drawn from the same centre.

1.3  Erecting a perpendicular.

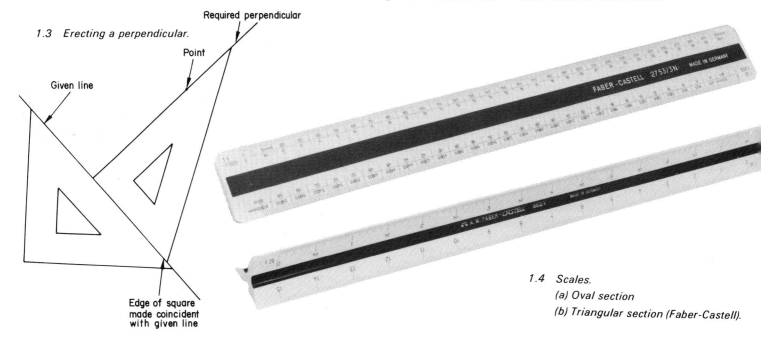

1.4  Scales.
(a) Oval section
(b) Triangular section (Faber-Castell).

A beam compass can either be a separate instrument on its own or in the form of an extension bar fitted to a compass or large springbow compass. Either way the purpose is to extend the size of radii that can be drawn. For large radii the beam compass is more accurate than an ordinary compass opened wide, because with the former there is no tendency for the arms to splay out when pressure is applied to the lead point.

**Springbow compass** (Fig. 1.6). Small radii up to about 40 mm are drawn using this instrument, although there are springbows which will open up to give radii much greater than this but conversely will not close down to draw the very small radii.

They can be set very accurately to a given radius by means of the small knurled wheel set between the compass legs.

On all compasses both the leads and points are replaceable. All leads should be sharpened on one side only.

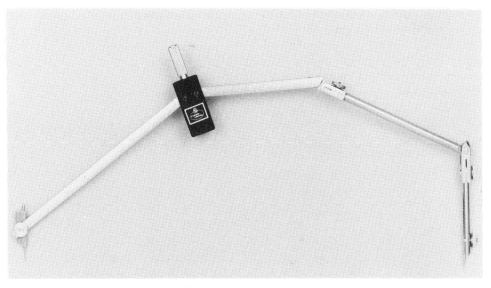

1.5 Large compass (Faber-Castell).

**Pencils** (1.7). Practically all drawings are made with a pencil even if at a later stage they are to be finished in ink.

There is a wide range of hardness of lead available and these are graded, B for soft leads and H for hard leads, an HB grade coming in the centre of the range. Pencils used on translucent material are generally of grade 2H for linework and F grade (between HB and H) for lettering. When using opaque paper, the most suitable grades are H or 2H for linework and HB or F for lettering, a lot depending on how heavy handed is the operator. Construction lines in all cases are best drawn with a pencil grade of not less than 3H.

There are wood-cased pencils, a mechanical type which grips the lead and fine lead holders. The first type requires the wood and lead to be constantly sharpened by means of a knife, not in a pencil sharpener. The second type has a piece of lead held in a mechanical clutch which can be quickly released to allow the lead to be changed or resharpened. Both of these types require the lead to be sharpened either to a conical point for lettering and sketching or to a chisel point for line drawing, the chisel form does not require sharpening as often as the conical one. Compass leads are sharpened on one side only – that which is remote from the point.

The third type, the fine lead holder (Fig. 1.7), does not need sharpening, a constant width of line is achieved by using a pencil with the appropriate lead diameter. The holder illustrated has an automatic lead feed, the push button being used only when a new lead is to be injected into the fine tube.

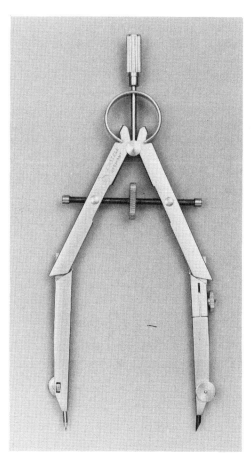

1.6 Springbow compass (Faber-Castell).

1.7 TK fine lead holder (Faber-Castell).

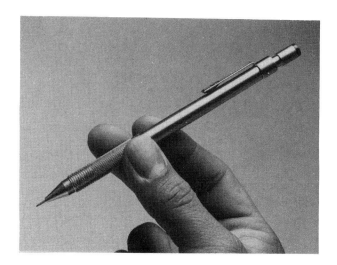

**Eraser** (Fig. 1.8). Pencil marks can be removed from most papers by using a good quality eraser without damaging the surface. Ink work will need a harder eraser and damage may be caused to the working surface depending on the type of drawing material being used. Ink marks on plastic film can be removed by scratching them out using a sharp knife or razor blade, but care must be taken to do this lightly otherwise holes will appear. Ink work on ordinary opaque drawing paper can be obliterated using 'Snopake'. When it has dried lines can be drawn over the painted area.

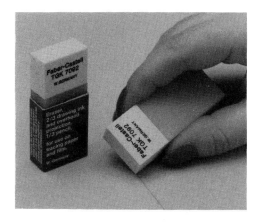

*1.8   Eraser for ink and pencil (Faber-Castell).*

Art gum blocks are very useful for cleaning up unwanted construction lines on finished drawings, they do however make a lot of crumbs.

**Erasing shield** (Fig. 1.9). If the work of the eraser is to be over a restricted area, particularly where there are numerous other lines, an erasing shield of thin metal or plastic can be used. An appropriate slot is placed over the portion to be removed thus preventing the eraser from removing adjacent linework.

Hard pencils can form a groove in the paper and it is difficult sometimes to remove the lead deposited at the bottom of this groove. This can

*1.9   Erasing shield.*

be overcome to some extent by placing a piece of hard material, such as a set square, under the drawing paper beneath the line to be removed and then using the eraser and shield the groove will be ironed out allowing the lead deposit to be rubbed out.

*1.10 Sandpaper block (Faber-Castell).*

**Sandpaper block** (Fig. 1.10). It has been seen that pencil and compass points need to be sharpened to a conical or chisel point at frequent intervals. This can be done using a very fine sandpaper block or well-worn metal file. Remember, sharpening in this way causes a lot of lead dust and this should be removed by knocking block or file into the wastepaper bin each time it is used.

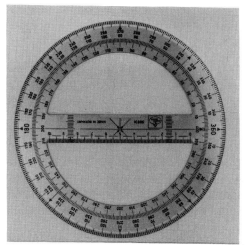

*1.11 360° protractor (Faber-Castell).*

**Protractor** (Fig. 1.11). Survey drawings frequently require angles to be set out to a lower degree of accuracy and this can be done by means of a protractor. There are two types, the half circle and the full 360°. The latter will be found to be more useful.

**Drawing board clips**. The drawing material is fixed to the drawing surface by means of spring clips or, if the drawing paper does not reach the limits of the board, by draughting tape. Drawing pins are *not* used as their continual use marks the drawing surface.

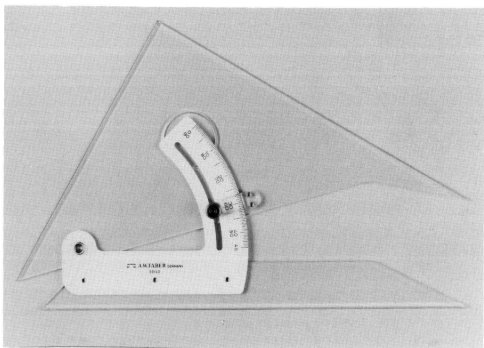

*1.12 Adjustable set square (Faber-Castell).*

**Duster**. It might seem strange to include a duster amongst drawing equipment, but it is a most essential part of the draughting profession. The drawing medium, tee square, set squares and all other equipment, including the pencil point after sharpening, must at all times be kept free of dust and eraser dirt. This is achieved by regularly wiping everything, hands included, with a clean duster or stockinette.

The remaining three items will be found useful at all stages of drawing office work and in the graphics to be done for other subjects in an engineering course.

**Adjustable set square** (Fig. 1.12). As the name implies, this square has an adjustable arm allowing the square to be set to an angle from 0° to 90°. With this square, the ordinary 45° set square can be dispensed with, but not the 30°/60° version. When set at this latter angle, the leg of the adjustable is not long enough.

**French curves and flexible curve** (Fig. 1.13). Two fundamental faults ruin a drawing – bad printing and badly drawn irregular curves. Smooth irregular curves can only be produced with the aid of a French curve or a flexible curve. A set of French curves consists of several shapes, bits of ellipses, parabolae and hyperbolae. The curves are made of wood or plastic, sometimes bevelled on one edge for ink use. The curve is moved round until one part fits the required shape, the curve, or one of the others in the set, may have to be moved about to complete an irregular shape.

The flexible curve can be shaped for a length of an irregular curve and it will retain its bent shape. Its disadvantage is that previous bends cannot always be completely removed.

**Pens** (Fig. 1.14). It is sometimes necessary to finish a drawing in ink, particularly in the case of illustrations or drawings forming documents for tenders or public enquiries, etc. General drawing office work uses ink far less these days than it used to because printing machines have now reached a very high standard of reproduction from pencil work.

Ink drawing is not easy and requires a lot of practice to reach an acceptable standard. Modern equipment in the form of technical drawing pens has helped considerably in this respect.

There are several technical pens manufactured but all revolve around a similar basic function. That is, there is a holder containing

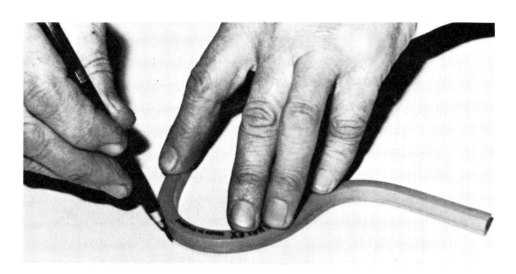

1.13 Drawing irregular curved lines.
(a) French curves (Jakar)
(b) Flexible curve (Jakar-flex).

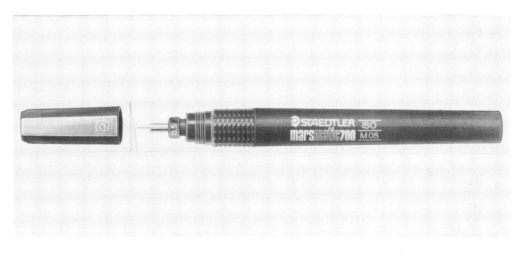

1.14 Technical drawing pen – Marsmatic 700.
(Staedtler U.K. Ltd)

drawing ink or a cartridge of ink which feeds the fluid to a fine tubular drawing point, permitting lines of equal thickness to be drawn. The nib units can be removed thus allowing a whole series of other nibs of different thickness to be used. Pens having nib sizes from 0.13 mm to 2.0 mm can be obtained. Compass attachments are also available for use with these pens.

A suitable set of pen sizes for general drawing use is:

0.35 mm for centre lines, dimensions and note leaders

0.5 mm for hidden edges

0.7 mm for visible edges.

Lettering, see also Chapter 3, can be done using these pens and suitable stencils, and there are also special stencils for a variety of everyday shapes which can be used with pen or pencil.

The old-type drawing pen (Fig. 1.15) is still available but it is less easy to operate in inexperienced hands.

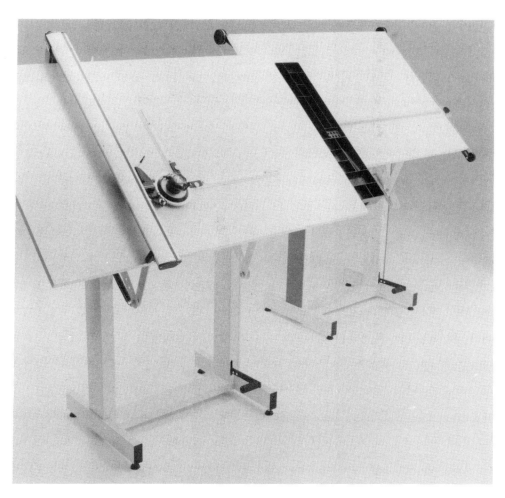

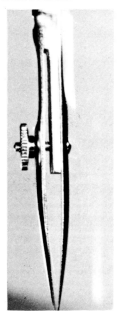

1.15 Drawing pen.

### (b) Materials on which drawings are made

Drawings can be made on paper and film, the latter being the most acceptable for ink work. At one time all ink work was done on linen cloth but the more stable plastic film has now taken over, being cheaper and easier to manipulate.

A reasonable quality cartridge paper will meet most student needs. It should have a surface that is smooth enough to take ink and yet strong enough to resist rubbing out. Detail

1.16 Left: Stand with medium draughting machine.
Right: Stand with parallel motion straight edge. (Supplied by Utopia Drawing Office Equipment Ltd)

paper is a thin, but strong, semi-transparent paper with a tough, smooth surface. It is used professionally for sketching out schemes in the design stage.

Tracing paper provides a tough, very smooth, working surface and will withstand plenty of rubbing out of pencil lines. It is more transparent than detail paper and will produce good dyeline prints, see Chapter 9, provided the pencil work is fairly dense. The best prints are obtained from drawings finished in ink.

### (c) Methods of supporting the drawing materials (Fig. 1.16)

The drawing medium, paper, film, etc., must at all times be supported on a flat surface which is stable. There are two categories for this:

(a) drawing board

(b) draughting machine.

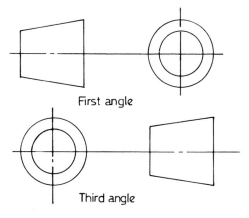

First angle

Third angle

1.17 BS symbols showing method of projection.

**Drawing board** (see Fig. 1.1). Drawing boards should preferably be battened and have a hard inset let into the working edge, along which the tee square slides if one is being used. There is a wide range of quality in boards, the cheap ones are made of plywood and suitable only for the lowest grade of work. Whilst most drawing offices in educational establishments provide boards for student use, it is desirable that a personal one is obtained. All work cannot be done away from home and, as has been mentioned already, practice is the only way to perfection.

Boards come in sizes slightly larger than the corresponding A size of paper that is to be used. In professional drawing offices boards of A0 size will be used but for the average student need an A1 size will be sufficient. For a sloped work surface raise board on a block.

Unless the board is to be equipped with some form of draughting machine, it will be necessary to use a tee square. This should be well constructed, the stock and the blade being well joined. The blade must be as long as the board and have the drawing edge bevelled. The stock must not be too short for when it is held against the board there must be no movement in the blade itself. Vertical lines are drawn by resting a set square along the blade, blade and set square being held firmly with one hand whilst the vertical line is drawn. When not in use, tee squares should be hung up using the hole provided in the blade.

A plain wood drawing board will need a backing sheet of paper beneath the drawing. This protects the surface of the board from the use of a hard pencil and also gives some resilience which is necessary when drawing.

**Draughting machines** (Fig. 1.16). Fundamentally they consist of a drawing board supported on a stand, which is adjustable both for height and inclination. The axes of the drawing can be provided by:

(a) a parallel motion straight edge and set squares
(b) a pantograph arm, or other system, with a drawing head.

The parallel motion type provides a straight edge that moves smoothly up and down the board, controlled possibly by wires. Set squares and adjustable squares are used in the same way as with a tee square. Not having to keep the straight edge firmly in place means there is

an increase in drawing speed.

Machines with a drawing head dispense with the use of set squares. They have two scales, which are interchangeable with different scale ratios, that are set at a right angle and the head can be rotated to any angle where it can be clamped. Some heads operate on a pantograph arm whilst others have a vertical and horizontal sliding system. A desired angle for the head is set by moving a part-graduated circle of degrees against a fixed mark or, as in a modern version, the angle is set from a digital protractor head with a liquid crystal display reading 5 minutes of arc.

## 1.3 FIRST STEPS IN DRAWING

The steps outlined below, whilst being simple, do, nevertheless, speed the work of preparing drawings.

(a) Attach paper to board with clips, using a backing sheet of paper if necessary. If the paper is too small to fill the board, draughting tape should be used.
(b) If paper is kept rolled up in a tube, see that it is done with the working face outwards, it will then be easier to control when fixed to the board.
(c) Complete the title block and draw a border to the paper if required.
(d) Observe the following procedure when making a drawing as it will provide a methodical approach, at the same time retaining neatness and accuracy with increased speed.
(i) Decide the arrangement on the paper of all the views required, spacing them out intelligently.
(ii) Insert the main centre or datum lines in all the views.
(iii) Draw in the required views lightly, building up the drawing from the centre or datum lines. Do not attempt to complete one view before moving to the next but build up parts of the object in all the views. Construction and projection lines should therefore be carried to other views wherever possible.
(iv) Clean up and check the drawing removing unwanted construction and projection lines.
(v) Line in circles and arcs before the straight lines, it is easier to connect a straight line to an arc than the other way

round.
(vi) Complete the lining in and again if this is done methodically (vertical lines, then horizontal lines and finally sloping lines) the drawing will be done that much quicker.
(vii) Insert dimensions and any notes.
(viii) Add section lines, titles and scale noting the type of projection used. On this latter point, at one time the type of projection used was spelled out, now the BS symbol is used (see Fig. 1.17).
(ix) At all times keep the pencil point sharp and make sure the instruments and paper are constantly wiped, removing dirt or rubber crumbs with a duster. You will find also that hands tend to collect dirt and should be washed quite frequently.
(x) Throughout the book reference will be made to BS 308, *Engineering Drawing Practice* – Parts 1, 2 and 3. This is the full standard relating to engineering drawing and it is an expensive publication. A condensed, and cheaper version, has been produced, PD/7308 *Engineering Drawing Practice for Schools and Colleges*. This introduces the students of technical drawing to the principles and conventions of BS 308.

## 1.4 ELEMENTARY DRAWING EXERCISES

These elementary drawing exercises are graded from straight line exercises through circular arcs to irregular curves needing French curves or flexible rulers.

The exercises are to test your precision, not your speed. Speed, which is important, can be gained later.

Make a complete drawing of the exercises, including a border and title panel with some printing and dimensions where appropriate. The newcomer to the drawing board can only gain confidence in the use of his equipment and learn his weaknesses, by plucking up the courage to attack the huge sheet of blank paper.

Use ink as soon as possible.

Use lines of different thickness and see the effect on the appearance of the drawing.

Perhaps the most revealing exercise is the 20 mm square subdivided into 2 mm squares. Lines irregularly spaced by only 0.1 mm will be all too obvious.

1.  Straight line exercises

(a)

Draw as many distinct lines in
10 mm as possible

(b)

Draw a grid of 2 mm squares.

(c)

Construct these letters in 15 mm squares.

2. Set square exercises

(a)

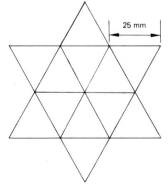

Set out with a 'sixty thirty' set square
and check the intersection of lines
at the centre.

(b)

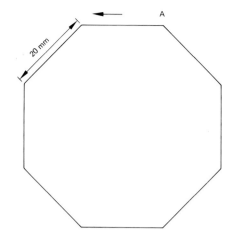

Start at A and go round the octagon
setting out the sides in order, to
see the error at A on completion.

3.  Compass and dividers exercises

(a)

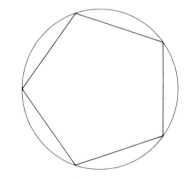

Pentagon in a circle of radius 25 mm
Divide the circumference by trial and error.

(b)

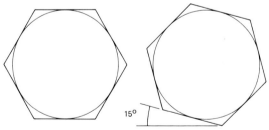

Draw a hexagon scribed round a circle of radius 25 mm

(c)

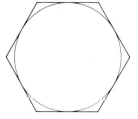

Draw a hexagon of sides 30 mm and inscribe a circle.

(d)

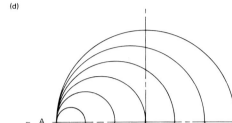

Copy this figure making A B 75 mm and then again 40 mm

4.   French curve exercises

(a)   Plot the two curves below.

| x (mm) | 0 | 10 | 20 | 30 | 40 | 50 | 60 | 70 | 80 | 90 |
|---|---|---|---|---|---|---|---|---|---|---|
| $y_1$ (mm) | 0 | 1 | 4 | 9 | 16 | 25 | 36 | 49 | 64 | 81 |
| $y_2$ (mm) | 0 | 2 | 8 | 18 | 32 | 50 | 72 | 98 | 128 | 162 |

(b)   Draw two ellipses (section 5.4 (b)) by the
        trammel method    (i)    60 mm x 40 mm
                               (ii)    150 mm x 50 mm.

(c)   Draw two parabolic arches (section 5.5 (a))
        (i)    30 mm span x 70 mm rise
        (ii)   200 mm span x 30 mm rise.

(d)   Draw a rectangular hyperbola
        (section 5.6) to pass through
        point P which has the co-ordinates
        100 mm 40 mm.

(e)

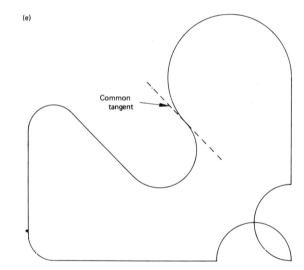

Common
tangent

Copy this figure (draw the radii first).

(f)

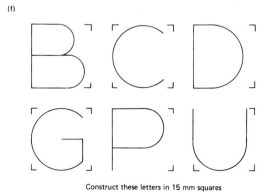

Construct these letters in 15 mm squares

# Chapter 2          **Projections**

*Below ground, a rock tunnel, part of the Awe Scheme. Drilling holes for further charges of explosive. Although the roughness of the roof shows that the rock strata was against the tunnellers, they have maintained a good tunnel profile. (Photograph supplied by George Wimpey & Co., Ltd.)*

## 2.1 INTRODUCTION

For centuries man tried to show his three-dimensional creations clearly and accurately by the two-dimensional medium of drawings. Three-dimensional pictures, sometimes with peculiar perspective, were used. While these still have their uses for qualitative description, they are inadequate for a complete definition of shape and almost useless for dimensions.

About the middle of the eighteenth century, a Frenchman, Gaspard Monge, realized that related two-dimensional views of solid objects should be projected from each other. It is the development of this technique that has become the engineer's international language. It seems inconceivable to us today that anything so simple could have evaded man's inquisitiveness for so long. The French soon realized what a powerful tool they had and managed to keep it a military secret for a quarter of a century.

The technique was brought to England by the father of I. K. Brunel who had been taught it when he was a naval cadet in France. Almost certainly the rapid spread of British technology in the nineteenth century was due to the ease with which engineers could communicate through their drawings with other engineers and with those engaged upon construction.

## 2.2 ORTHOGRAPHIC PROJECTION

A complete record of an object can be made photographically if enough pictures are taken to include all important details. If the photographs are taken with little planning some of the required detail may be missed while other parts will be duplicated. Moreover, unless the camera is held level, vertical lines will converge or diverge, see Fig. 2.1.

However, if the camera is set up carefully so that photographs are taken on three axes at right angles to each other, every bit of detail will be recorded in six views; above, below, front, back, and the two sides, as shown in Fig. 2.2 from which the bottom view has been omitted. The fundamental rules of orthographic projection have been observed, although the photographs themselves display distortion due to perspective effects and are not true or orthographic views.

The three-dimensional views, Fig. 2.1, give an instant impression of the model car, but its true proportions can only be obtained from the orthographic views in Fig. 2.2. This applies

also to drawings of civil engineering structures.

## 2.3 THIRD ANGLE PROJECTION

True two-dimensional views can be obtained simply on the drawing board. One method of doing this is shown in Fig. 2.3. A solid object is set up inside an imaginary transparent cube, with its axes parallel to the faces of the cube. It is viewed through each face of the cube in turn on axes normal to the faces of the cube. As the lines projecting the outline on to the faces of the cube are parallel, the outline will be the same size as the original.

In this way, six orthographic views of the object can be obtained. As most engineering

*2.1 Random three-dimensional views of a model car which give an instant impression of it but are useless for correct proportions and dimensions.*

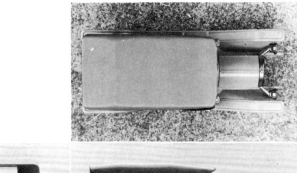

2.2  Five related 'orthographic' views of a
model car which show its proportions
and could be used for dimensions. The
interpretation of the general shape of
such a familiar object is not difficult
from these views, but less well known
objects are more difficult to visualize
without practice.

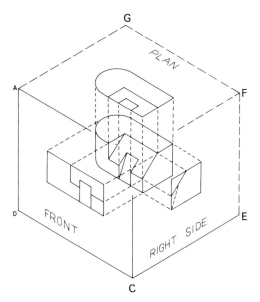

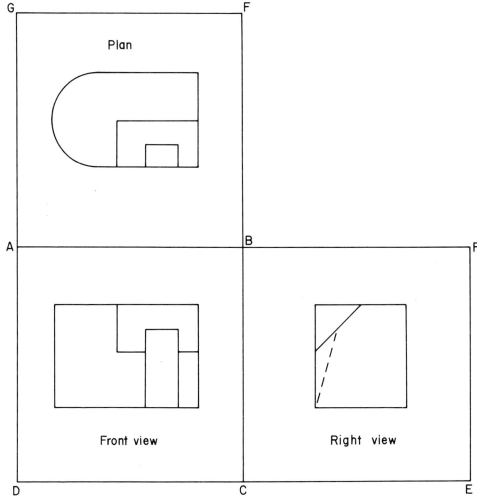

2.3  An object inside a cube, with its axes
parallel to the faces of the cube. Orthographic views have been projected on to
the faces of the cube for third angle
projection.

2.4  Faces of the cube in Fig. 2.3 laid out flat
to give conventional third angle projection.

shapes have some symmetry, it is usually found that three views are sufficient to describe the shape completely: the plan, the front view, and one of the side views. Strictly, two views would describe any object if all hidden detail is shown by dotted lines, but the result would be confusing. Hidden detail of any complexity is best shown by another view or section. Pedantic use of dotted lines to show all hidden detail should be avoided.

Obtaining the required two-dimensional views on the face of a cube is only half of the problem. They must now be conventionally arranged on a plane so that dimensions can be transferred from one view to another and a trained eye can quickly infer the shape of the object.

The generally accepted way of doing this is third angle projection. Imagine that the cube in Fig. 2.3 is cut along its dotted edges and hinged along the edges shown by solid lines. Now swing point G across to lie on DA produced and swing point E across to lie on DC produced. Figure 2.4 shows the cube laid out flat in this way. This is third angle projection.

The PLAN is vertically above the FRONT VIEW and the RIGHT SIDE must be level with the FRONT VIEW.

Careful orientation of the object within the cube will help the presentation. It is better if long objects are placed so that their length is shown in both the plan and front view, see Fig. 2.5 (a), since the finished set of views will then fit into the normal horizontal format of a drawing sheet. In Fig. 2.5 (b), the plan is drawn with its longer axis vertical. This crowds the views vertically and wastes space at each end of the drawing.

### Why call it third angle projection?

Although there can only be one orthographic or true view of each face of a three-dimensional object, the three views generally necessary for unambiguous shape description can be arranged in several ways.

There are four basic arrangements of the orthographic views of an object. These are obtained by putting the object into one of the four named quadrants shown in Fig. 2.6. Whichever quadrant is used, the plan is viewed from above and the front view from the right, thereby causing the images in third angle projection to be brought back on to their respective planes of projection. In first angle projection, they are projected forward.

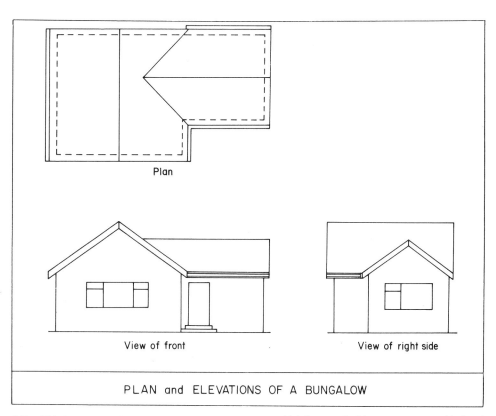

Plan

View of front          View of right side

PLAN and ELEVATIONS OF A BUNGALOW

2.5   Third angle projection of a bungalow.
      (a) Suitable arrangement (above)—
          long axes of the object parallel to
          the long axes of the drawing.

(b) Less suitable arrangement (below)
    —long axes of the object parallel
    to the short axes of the drawing
    resulting in the bad use of the
    available space.

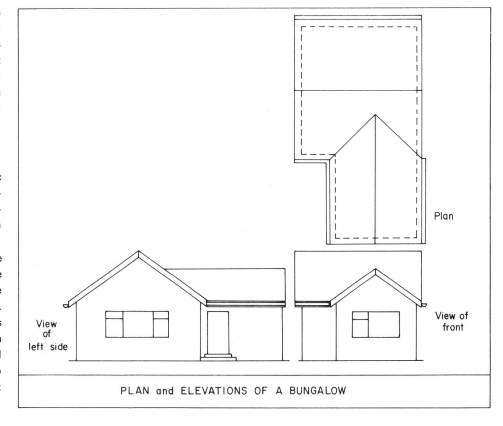

Plan

View of left side          View of front

PLAN and ELEVATIONS OF A BUNGALOW

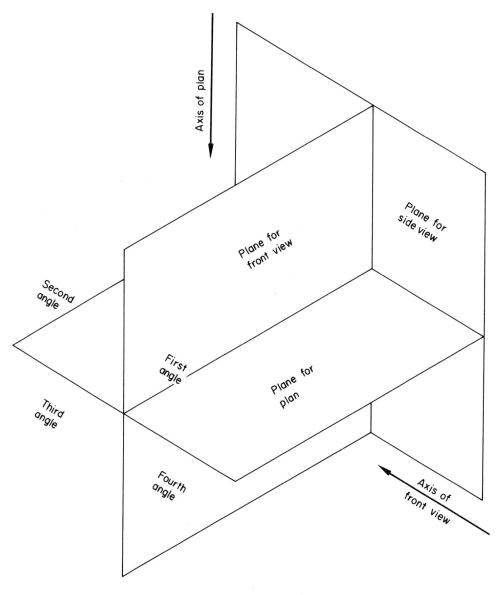

2.6   *The four possible angles for projection showing the lines of sight for plans and front views.*

Second and fourth angle projection seem never to have been used.

In BS 1192: 1953, the first angle method is defined as the European standard, with the exception of Holland, while the third angle method is ascribed to America and Holland. Third angle projection has been adopted throughout this text. However, as will be seen later, civil engineers are driven to various expedients in projection in order to portray the large objects they design and build.

Figure 2.7 (a) shows an object in the first quadrant with the three views projected on to their respective planes, while (b) shows the planes laid out flat revealing the first angle arrangement of the basic views.

Figure 2.8 compares first angle (a) and third angle (b) projections with a combination of the two (c).

## 2.4 COMBINED PROJECTION. BRITISH STANDARD PROJECTION

The following quotations from BS 1192: *Drawing Office Practice for Architects and Builders* show the British genius for compromise:

Third angle projection has the advantage that the features of adjacent views are in juxtaposition, and thus it is easier than in first angle projection to project one view from the other when drawing, and also easier to associate those features when dimensioning or reading the drawing.

. However (according to the BS) many feel that the plan should be located below the front view and this has given rise to a combination of first and third angle projection.

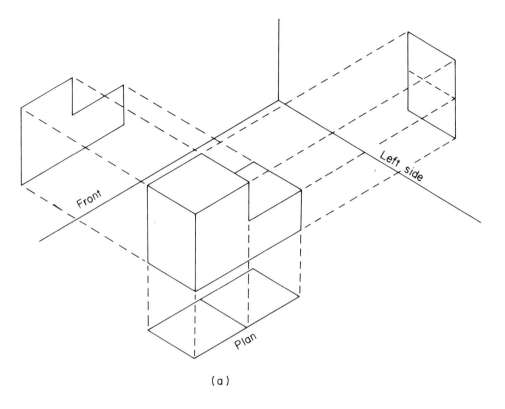

(a)

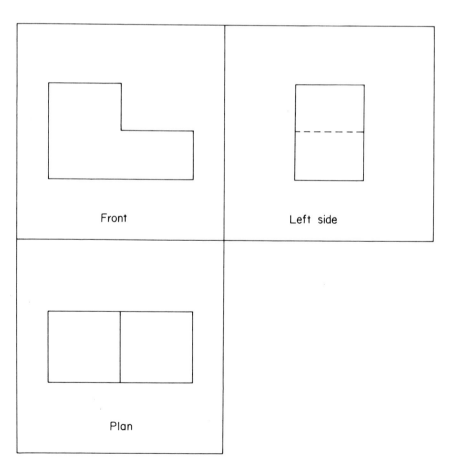

(b)

2.7 First angle projection.
   (a) How the orthographic views are cast forward to the planes of projection.
   (b) The resulting conventional arrangement when the cube is laid out flat.

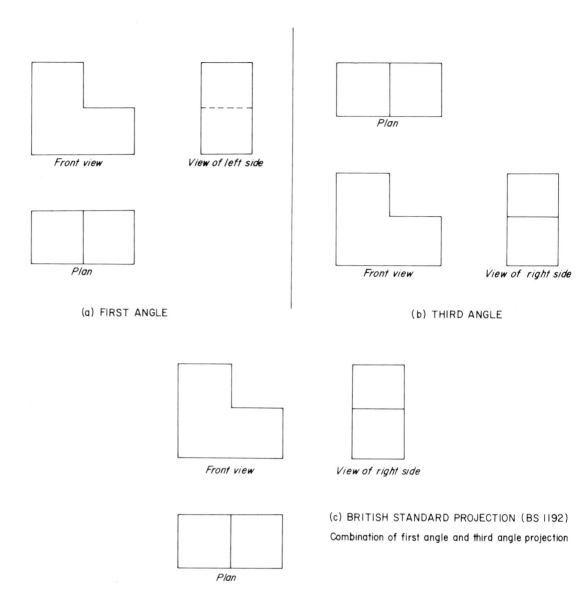

(a) FIRST ANGLE

*Front view*    *View of left side*

*Plan*

(b) THIRD ANGLE

*Plan*

*Front view*    *View of right side*

*Front view*    *View of right side*

*Plan*

(c) BRITISH STANDARD PROJECTION (BS 1192)
Combination of first angle and third angle projection

*2.8   Comparison of projections.*

In relation to the elevation, end views are placed so that they are in third angle projection and plan views in first angle projection.

For building drawings this method has been practised very widely and combines the advantage of both first and third angle projection.

It is recommended that all elevations should be properly identified, either with descriptive notes, or joined with projection lines or by some other suitable means.

## 2.5 APPLICATION OF ORTHOGRAPHIC PROJECTION

All rules are made to be broken so long as the discipline behind them is understood.

In Fig. 2.9 the general outline of a simple structure is shown, with the three views laid out strictly in accordance with the rules of

third angle projection. The views themselves, however, have been modified in order to show structural detail more clearly.

The plan is quite straightforward, there is very little hidden detail which has all been shown.

A longitudinal section on the centre line is shown in place of a normal front view. As this particular structure is buried in the ground, a normal front view would be seen through the ground so that the entire view would consist of hidden detail and give rise to a confusing mass of dotted lines.

Similarly, a normal side view would show too much hidden detail, most of which would be buried in shading showing earth in section, therefore a sectional view has been used instead.

Owing to the shape of the flume and the profile of the water as it flows through it, the

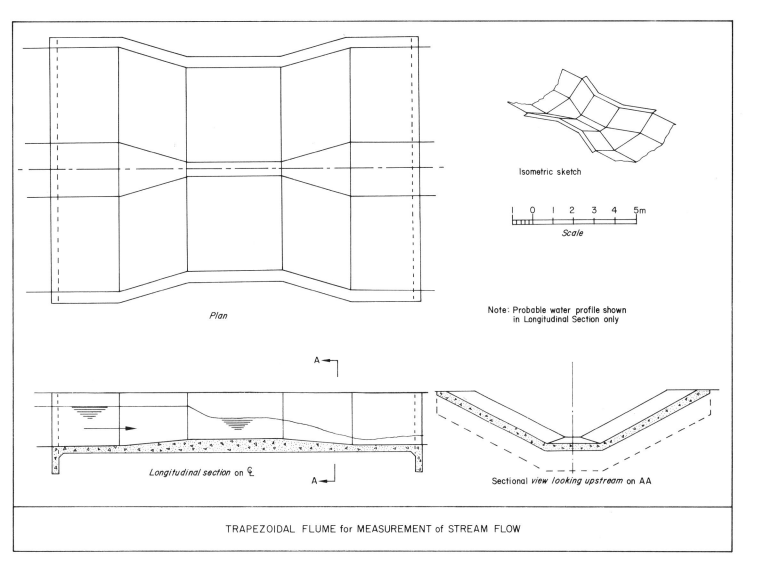

Isometric sketch

|— 0 | 2 3 4 5m

*Scale*

*Plan*

Note: Probable water profile shown
in Longitudinal Section only

A →

*Longitudinal section on ℄*

A →

*Sectional view looking upstream* on AA

TRAPEZOIDAL FLUME for MEASUREMENT of STREAM FLOW

plan view of the water surface would be complicated therefore it has been omitted, but a note stating this has been added. This expedient has also saved the time that would otherwise have been spent in preparing the curves of intersection.

Most civil engineering schemes include structures which are too large to be shown by the conventional application of third angle projection, therefore the rules have to be broken. Figure 2.10 shows the outline of an earth dam, fundamentally a very simple structure to draw, but too large for the side views (represented by cross sections) to be shown alongside the front view. The required cross section is shown below but is carefully referenced.

An earth dam is quite simple and its detail can sometimes be shown to a scale small enough for it all to be contained on one drawing. More complicated structures will have to

be shown on a larger scale to resolve their detail and thus will spread to several drawings.

However useless it may be for dimensions and small detail, a small drawing of a large project, giving several related views on one sheet, can be very useful for showing the whole scheme to lay observers. This type of drawing will probably be valued by senior engineers who have not the time to digest several drawings but who, nevertheless, must know the overall pattern of the scheme.

**2.6 SECTIONS**

It is frequently necessary to show a structure in section, i.e., cut open, either to help with the general presentation, as with the flume in Fig. 2.9, or to show internal detail, as with the earth dam in Fig. 2.10.

The symbolic shading of sections is described in Chapter 3, but must be applied with discretion and should not be allowed to over-

2.9    *Suitable method of using third angle projection to show a small and simple structure.*

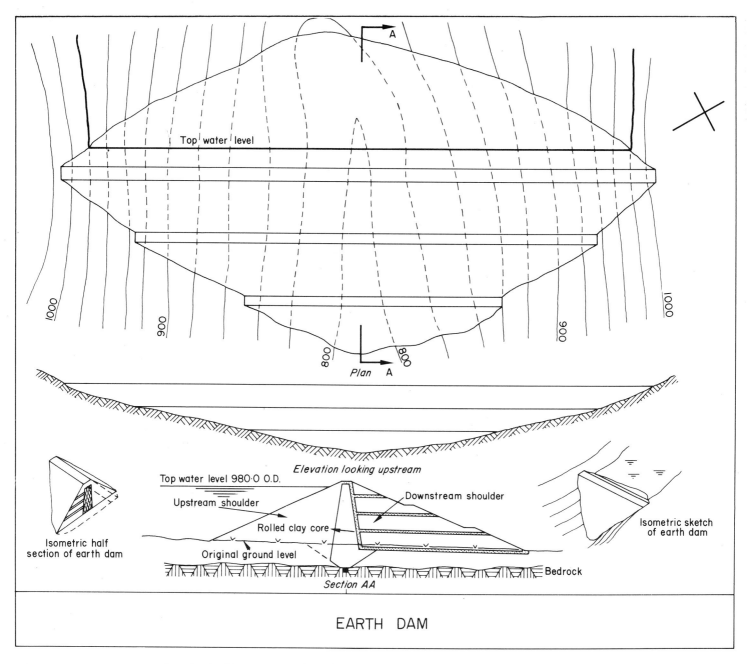

**EARTH DAM**

2.10 *Suitable arrangement of orthographic views of a large structure.*

power other detail. For example, with the concrete retaining wall in Fig. 2.11, where a relatively large expanse of sectioned concrete must be shown, the whole effect is lightened by shading selected patches and leaving quite large areas clear. Such techniques may be used, so long as the required effect is obtained and there is no possibility of error. Areas should be left free for dimensions, some hidden detail, or other symbols.

While the symbolic shading immediately identifies a section, the location of a section can only be shown by references in other views. Unless a section is a particularly awkward one, it is seldom necessary for the lines

of the cut to be superimposed on the detail of the view in which the location of the section is shown. The location can usually be shown by short, heavy reference lines outside the general detail, as shown in Fig. 2.10. Arrows should show the direction from which the section is viewed.

Sometimes one section can do the work of two or perhaps more by changing the line of cut at suitable points. If a section does wander in this way, its precise line must be shown in another view, see Fig. 2.12.

The layout of any drawing must be carefully planned in advance. This is particularly important when choosing sections. They must

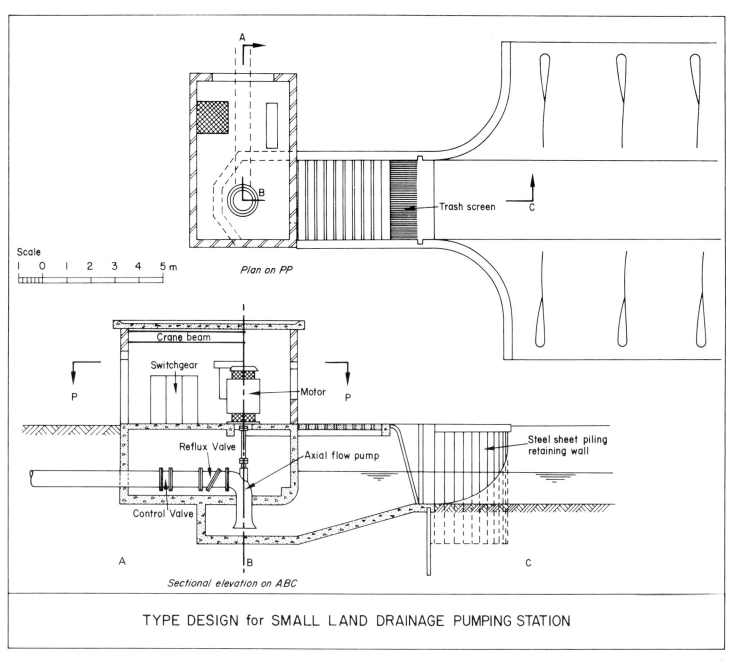

A

B

Scale
1  0  1  2  3  4  5 m

*Plan on PP*

Trash screen

C

Crane beam

Switchgear

Motor

P                                                                                    P

Reflux Valve

Axial flow pump

Steel sheet piling
retaining wall

Control Valve

A                          B                                                         C

*Sectional elevation on ABC*

## TYPE DESIGN for SMALL LAND DRAINAGE PUMPING STATION

be selected early in the drawing process so
that reference lines can be shown before other
detail is added to avoid possible confusion.

### 2.7 AUXILIARY VIEWS

It sometimes happens that because of the
irregularity of its outline, the true shape of one
or more faces of an object cannot be shown
in any of the normal orthographic views. This
will occur when the face to be shown is not
parallel to one of the axes chosen for pro-
jective purposes. The solution is to project
a view from the face in question on lines
normal to the face into a suitable space on
the drawing, as shown in Fig. 2.13 (a).

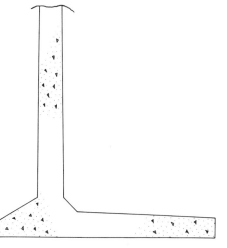

2.12   *Plan and section of a small land drainage
pumping station. Note how the section
is taken on the line ABC in the plan.*

2.11   *Section of a reinforced concrete retaining wall with conventional shading
limited in extent for lighter effect.*

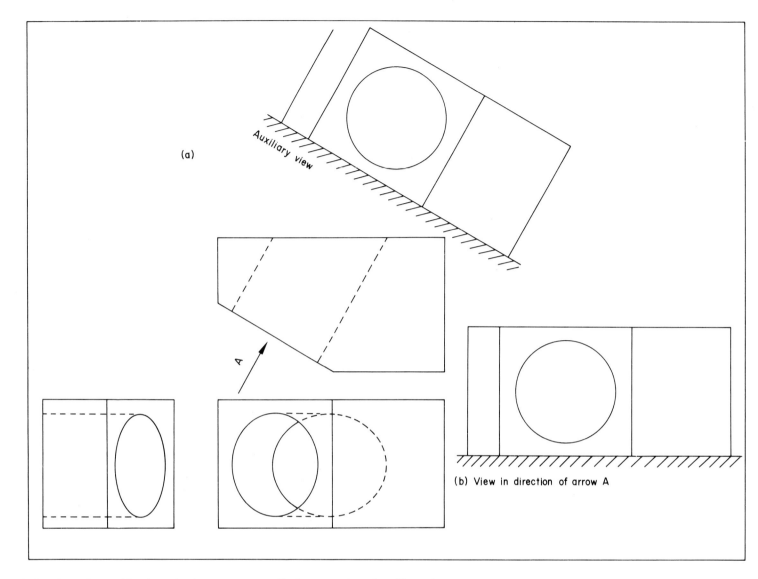

(a)

Auxiliary view

A

(b) View in direction of arrow A

2.13  *The orthographic view of a face, not on the axes of projection, projected on to an auxiliary plane.*
   *(a) Conventionally.*
   *(b) In a more practical manner.*

If a large number of auxiliary views seem to be necessary, rearrangement of the object within the planes of projection may help to reduce the number.

Although civil engineers should be capable of projecting auxiliary views as shown in Fig. 2.13 (a), they may never use the technique in practice. Once again, the size of the objects to be depicted mitigates against the strict observance of the rules of projection. Whether there is space on a drawing to project a view at an angle or not, it is inconvenient to have views at odd angles on a drawing, especially if the drawing is large and has to be folded for use on a windswept site.

The usual procedure is to indicate, by a heavy arrow on the plan, the line on which the auxiliary view is seen and then to locate the view on the same axes as the rest of the drawing and to label it, for example, 'View in direction of arrow A', see Fig. 2.13 (b).

## 2.8 PICTORIAL DRAWING

If the object being drawn is at all complicated, or it must be described to a lay observer who has not been trained in orthographic projection, a reversion to three-dimensional illustration is necessary. In some cases a quick, free-hand sketch will be sufficient, but more complicated examples will require some formalized technique if proportion and scale are to be maintained.

True three-dimensional illustration shows perspective. This is dealt with in Chapter 6. There are several simpler and quicker ways of showing depth without the complication of perspective.

### (a) Oblique projection

Perhaps the quickest pictorial method is oblique projection, which consists, in essence, of adding bogus depth to an orthographic front view of an object, see Fig. 2.14.

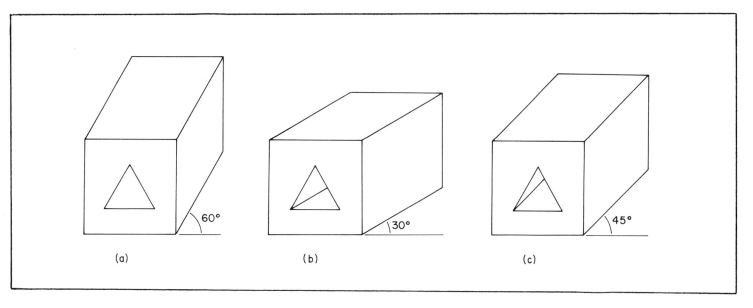

(a)                                   (b)                                   (c)

As the top and sides of an oblique projection are badly distorted, it is essential that the orthographic view chosen as the basis for the illustration should contain the details to be clarified.

The receding axis can be at any angle to the front view and can be varied to show more of the top or more of the side, see Fig. 2.14 (a) and (b). Unless a particular face is to be accentuated, the receding axis should be at 45°, see Fig. 2.14 (c).

### (b) Axonometric projection

Axonometric projection, as shown in Fig. 2.15, is sometimes used by architects.

Like oblique projection, a bogus effect of depth is obtained by adding a third dimension to an orthographic view, the plan in the example shown. If the orthographic plan view is set at an angle to the horizontal axis of the drawing, more than one face of the object can be shown.

Although a remarkably realistic impression is obtained with little complication, the use of true heights makes the building look too tall. A simple halving of the vertical measurements as shown reduces the height too much, three-quarters scale would perhaps be better. A more realistic effect could be obtained by using isometric projection without recourse to differential scales.

### (c) Isometric projection

A true three-dimensional effect can only be obtained if all the faces of the object are at an angle to the plane of projection and, therefore, suffer distortion.

Surprisingly, if a cube is put on a table and viewed so that all the faces are at an angle to the line of vision, the infinite number of different views fall into only three categories. These are shown in Fig. 2.16.

In isometric projection, the cube is viewed symmetrically so that all its edges seem to be of the same length, that is they must all be at the same angle to the plane of projection. As the name isometric implies, there is equal measure, all the sides are of the same length.

In dimetric projection, the viewpoint remains on the central axis but is lowered slightly or raised so that the top of the cube is foreshortened or made to look longer. In this way, the edges of the cube appear with two different lengths in the projection, 'two measures' in fact as the name infers.

Trimetric projection results from completely random or asymmetrical viewing of the cube so that the sides on all three axes of the cube appear with different lengths and there are 'three measures'.

Dimetric and trimetric projection are seldom used. If such a complication is warranted, it is

2.14  Oblique projection where depth is given to an orthographic view by running adjacent surfaces back an arbitrary distance at any suitable angle.

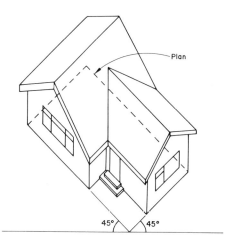

2.15  Axonometric projection where realistic but arbitrary depth is given to an orthographic plan view

2.16  Comparison of geometric three-dimensional projections.

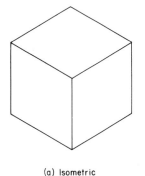

(a) Isometric

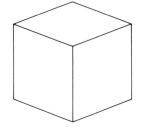

(b) Dimetric

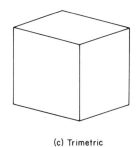

(c) Trimetric

probably worthwhile making a perspective drawing as described in Chapter 6.

Figure 2.17 shows, in third angle orthographic projection, a cube set up at an angle to a plane to produce an isometric projection.

The front view and plan show how the opposite corners of the cube, A and G, are on a line normal to the plane of projection. In this position, all the edges of the cube are at an angle $\theta$ to the plane of projection.

The side view in Fig. 2.17 is, in fact, the isometric projection. The plan is not. It is dimetric, as the edges make two different angles with a horizontal plane of projection.

In the isometric projection in Fig. 2.17 the three adjacent edges of the cube AB, AE, and AD, representing the three axes of the cube, are equally spaced at 120° round the point A, which is in contact with the plane of projection. This is the basis of all isometric construction. Figure 2.18 shows how the axes can be set up at any angle so long as they are equally spaced round a central point.

It will be seen in the isometric view, which is the right side view in Fig. 2.17, that although the three edges, AB, AE, and AD have the same length, the two diagonals, AC and BD, do not, although they are the same length as each other in the original cube. There must, therefore, be some axes on which measurements can be made, and some axes which suffer distortion and cannot be used for measurement. The principal axes of the cube, represented by the edges AB, AE, and AD, are the only ones that do not distort and are, therefore, the only ones on which measurements can be made. Points on the faces of the cube away from the edges must be located by offset measurements from the edges, see Fig. 2.22.

**Isometric scale.** If an isometric drawing is being used by itself as a pictorial representation of the object, the actual measurements of the object or true dimensions can be used for plotting along the isometric axes. However, if the isometric view is to be used alongside the orthographic views it is to clarify, the dimensions for the isometric view must be reduced to cos $\theta$ times their true value otherwise it will appear very much larger than the orthographic views and will be misleading, see Fig. 2.19.

To determine the value of $\theta$ and cos $\theta$ refer to Fig. 2.17 and consider the sides of the cube to be x units long. The length of the diagonal

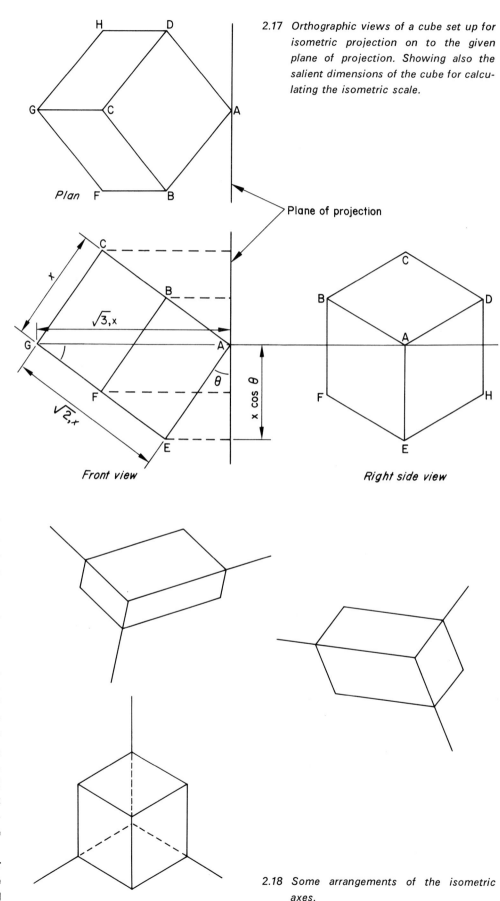

2.17  *Orthographic views of a cube set up for isometric projection on to the given plane of projection. Showing also the salient dimensions of the cube for calculating the isometric scale.*

2.18  *Some arrangements of the isometric axes.*

of a side is $\sqrt{2.x}$, while the opposite corners of the cube are $\sqrt{3.x}$ apart (by application of Pythagoras' theorem).

Hence $\cos \theta$ is

$$\frac{\sqrt{2.x}}{\sqrt{3.x}} \quad \text{or} \quad \sqrt{\frac{2}{3}} \quad \text{or } 0.816,$$

or $\theta = 35°16'$.

Thus for a realistic view, all measurements should be reduced to 0.816 times their true value before being used in an isometric projection. This can most easily be done graphically, as shown in Fig. 2.20. Measure the true length along the line inclined at 45° and drop a perpendicular to the line inclined at 30°, which will then contain the isometric length.

**Circles in isometric projection.** Figure 2.21 is an isometric view of a cube with circles on the three visible faces. The circles appear as ellipses with their major axis parallel to the longer diagonal of the cube face.

As isometric projection is a pictorial impression, an approximate construction of the ellipses is justified.

An ellipse can be approximated to two pairs of circular arcs, see section 5.4 (d). In isometric work, the arcs span the spaces between the isometric axes. In Fig. 2.21 the arcs will be seen to span the spaces between X and Y and also between XX and YY. Here is a quick method of drawing the ellipses:

(a) Set off the diameter along an isometric axis, lines XY.

(b) Draw the enveloping quadrilateral ABCD.

(c) Draw the diagonals of the enveloping quadrilaterals, these will contain the major and minor axes of the ellipse.

(d) Join the corner A of the enveloping quadrilateral to the ends of the diameters X.

(e) The centres P of the smaller arcs are at the intersection of lines AX and line BD.

(f) The larger circular arcs have their centres at the obtuse corners of the enveloping quadrilaterals.

Remember that this is a quick, approximate method. The ellipses so formed deviate from the exact shape in some places and will not always meet straight lines drawn by offset methods as they should. If much of the picture is a combination of curves and straight lines, the whole should be constructed by offsets, see the next section.

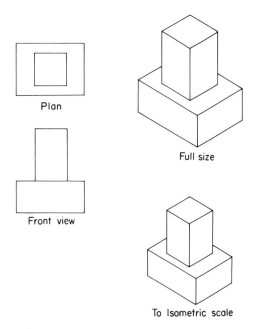

Full size

Front view

Plan

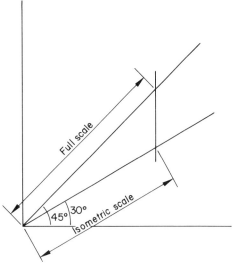

To Isometric scale

2.19 *The greater realism of an isometric view drawn to isometric scale than one drawn full size, in comparison with orthographic views.*

2.20 *Graphical construction of isometric scale.*

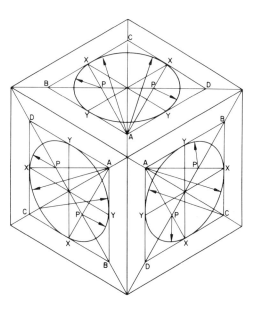

2.21 *Circles in isometric projection. Showing the construction of ellipses on three faces of a cube.*

**Irregular shapes in isometric projection.** It is convenient to classify any shape, other than a circle, as irregular for isometric projection since the method of construction is the same: to envelope the shape in a square or rectangle orientated to lie on the isometric axes. Measurements can be made along the sides of the enveloping rectangle to locate the points necessary to draw the shape.

In Fig. 2.22 a parabola, drawn in this way, is shown. Points 1, 2, 3, 4, 5, and 6 are located by means of offsets from sides AD, BC and AO, OB which can be drawn on the isometric axes without distortion.

Figure 2.23 shows two orthographic views of an hexagonal nut. In the plan view, the nut is shown enveloped by a rectangle ABCD which is then drawn on the isometric axes. The corners X of the nut can be located by measurements along the isometric axes. The circular hole is represented by an ellipse with its major axis horizontal.

## 2.9 INTERPRETING ENGINEERING DRAW-INGS—VISUALIZATION EXERCISES

An engineer reads and interprets many more drawings than he produces himself. His own drawings are the result of a close study of other drawings. If he is well trained in projection, he quickly builds up a useful mental image of a scheme from a strange set of drawings. This is rather different from the slower process of producing orthographic views of his own ideas.

The following exercises, making three-dimensional views from orthographic ones and vice versa, are designed to sharpen your understanding of the conventions of projection laid down in this chapter.

Isometric sketches are quickly and accurately made freehand on isometric paper, i.e., paper printed with axes 120° apart, which is available in blocks. Orthographic or oblique views are made more quickly and neatly on paper with lightly printed 5 mm squares.

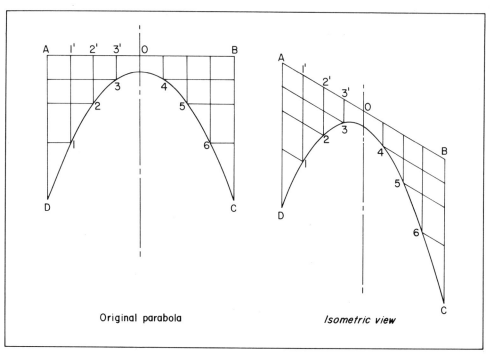

Original parabola                    *Isometric view*

2.22 *Construction of irregular curved shapes in isometric views by offsets from the isometric axes, seen applied to a parabola.*

2.23 *Construction of irregular plane shapes in isometric views by offsets from an enveloping rectangle that can be constructed on the isometric axes.*

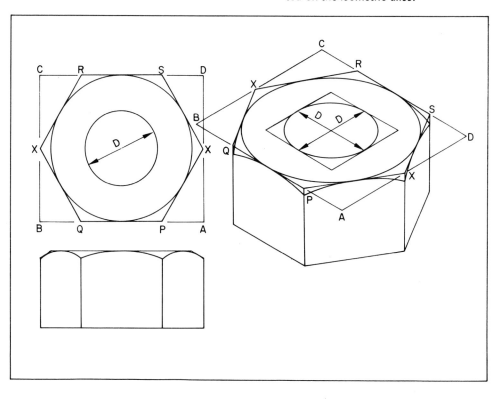

**2.10 EXERCISES.**

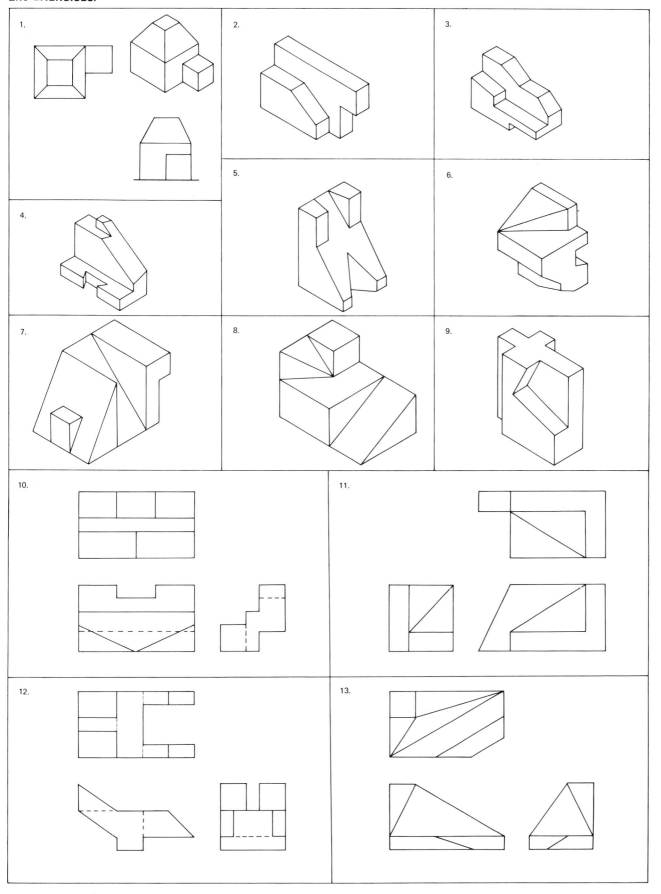

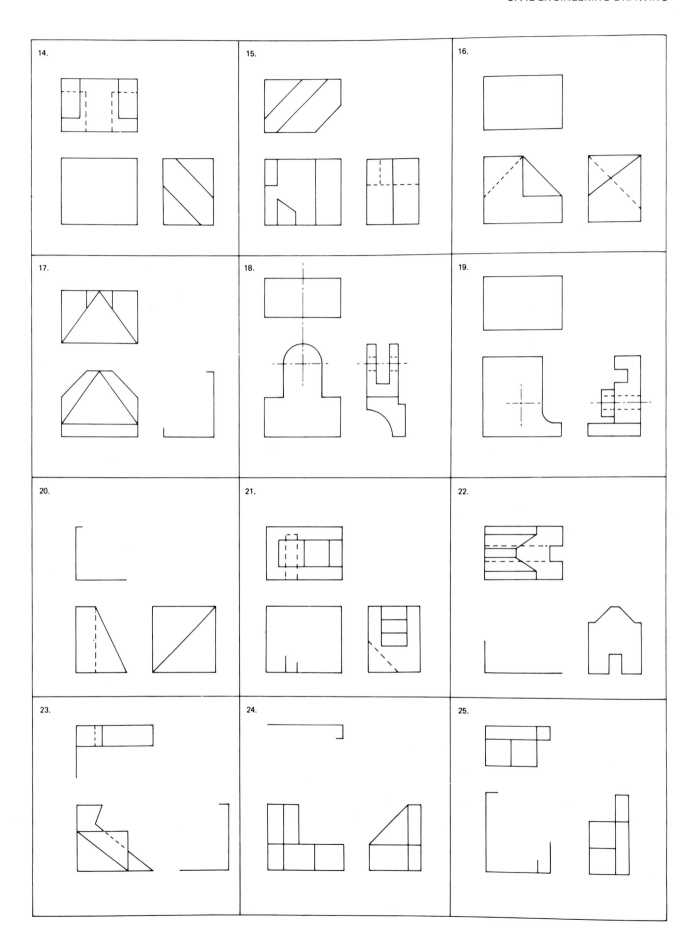

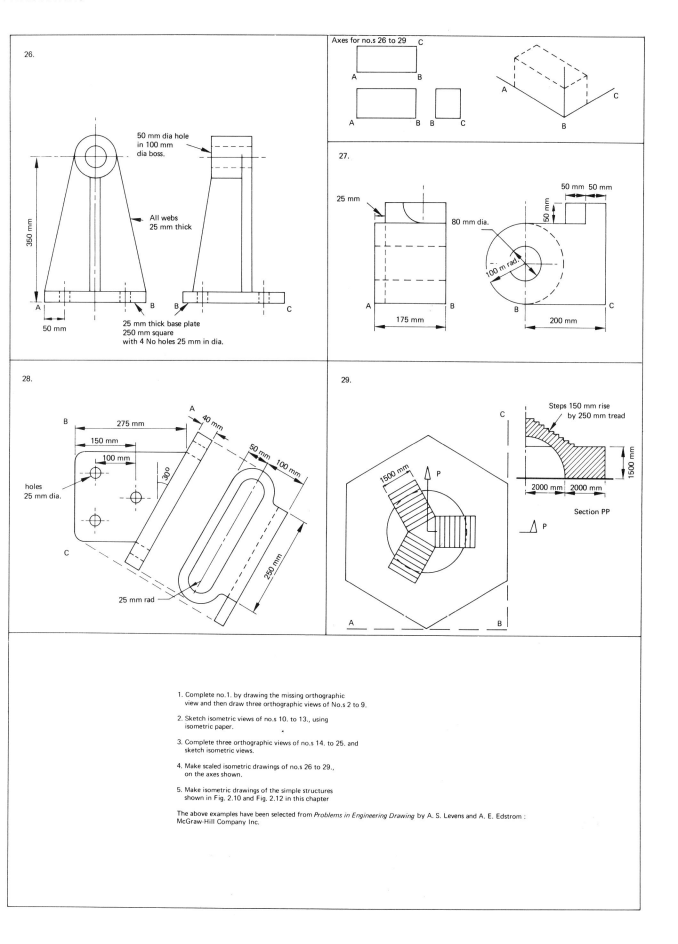

1. Complete no.1. by drawing the missing orthographic
   view and then draw three orthographic views of No.s 2 to 9.

2. Sketch isometric views of no.s 10. to 13., using
   isometric paper.

3. Complete three orthographic views of no.s 14. to 25. and
   sketch isometric views.

4. Make scaled isometric drawings of no.s 26 to 29.,
   on the axes shown.

5. Make isometric drawings of the simple structures
   shown in Fig. 2.10 and Fig. 2.12 in this chapter

The above examples have been selected from *Problems in Engineering Drawing* by A. S. Levens and A. E. Edstrom :
McGraw-Hill Company Inc.

# Chapter 3      **Conventions and presentation**

*Wimbleball Reservoir Dam. (Photograph supplied by the New Civil Engineer)*

## 3.1 INTRODUCTION

Conventions range from the type of line and printing to be used on a drawing, through formalized shading of sections, to the widely used and understood conventional signs of *Ordnance Survey* maps.

Presentation is concerned with the overall appearance of the finished drawing. It can be influenced by the position of the views within the available space on the paper, the thickness and variety of the lines used, the type of printing, etc. An engineer will leave something of himself in each of his drawings; his style and presentation will be different in detail from that of his colleagues. Some people have a happy flair for layout, while others struggle hard and achieve less elegant results.

A few of the more important conventions and details of presentation are considered in this chapter. Many of the items are further described in the three British Standards, BS 308: *Engineering Drawing Practice*, BS 1192: *Drawing Office Practice for Architects and Builders*, and BS 3429: *Specification for Sizes of Drawing Sheets*. Where possible a direct quotation or illustration from the appropriate British Standard is used.

## 3.2 SIZES OF DRAWINGS (BS 3429)

The metric or A sizes of drawings are listed in Table 3.1, with reference to some of the approximate Imperial sizes with their resounding names.

The basic metric size, A0, is a rectangle of one square metre with its sides in the ratio of 1: $\sqrt{2}$. Derived sizes are either successively halved or doubled, but still retain the same ratio of long side to short side. In this way, smaller sheets can be made from larger ones without waste. This was not always possible with the old Imperial sizes.

The A1 size is slightly larger and, therefore, more convenient to use, than the Imperial size formerly used by most students. The A4 size is used for reports and lecture notes.

Most engineering drawing will be on the A0 size, which replaces the popular double elephant (30 x 40 in.) and the longer antiquarian (30 x 53 in.).

The larger the drawing the smaller the number of drawings required to cover a given scheme. There is a move towards smaller, more precise drawings which are more convenient to handle. Engineers, who have had to manage large drawings on a windy site in

| | | | | | |
|---|---|---|---|---|---|
| 4 A0 | 1682 x 2378 mm | | | | |
| 2 A0 | 1189 x 1682 mm | Hamburg | (40 x 60 in.) | 1015 x 1530 mm | |
| A0 | 841 x 1189 mm | Double elephant | (30 x 40 in.) | 763 x 1015 mm | |
| A1 | 594 x 841 mm | Imperial | (20 x 30 in.) | 508 x 763 mm | |
| A2 | 420 x 594 mm | | | | |
| A3 | 297 x 420 mm | | | | |
| A4 | 210 x 297 mm | Foolscap | ( 8 x 13 in.) | 203 x 330 mm | |

Table 3.1

the rain or in a car, will appreciate why this movement has started.

Strip plans of roads or rivers, with their associated cross sections, are more convenient on small drawings, A2, A3, or A4, clipped together in album form. Moreover, there is less chance of the drawings being damaged in use.

Although many existing drawings could quite well be presented serially on small sheets, the common procedure is to use larger scale ratios and more precise drawing techniques. Many large drawings waste space which represents time and money.

Amendments can be made more easily by redrawing a whole, small sheet rather than by laboriously erasing large parts of a conventional drawing. Rush jobs can flow from the drawing office in a fairly steady stream of small drawings rather than in gulps as they often do when the more conventional method is used.

## 3.3 LAYOUT

It is recommended that the standard layout for contract and working drawings should be as shown (in Fig. 3.1).

It is recognised that latitude may be necessary in the arrangement of title and revision panels, notes, etc., to meet differing requirements, but it is considered that a standard layout of sheet will facilitate the reading of drawings and make it possible for essential references to be located easily, especially when drawings are prepared by several offices. A standard arrangement tends to ensure that all necessary information is included. (BS 1192)

A particular firm may have good reasons for keeping its established drawing layout, but

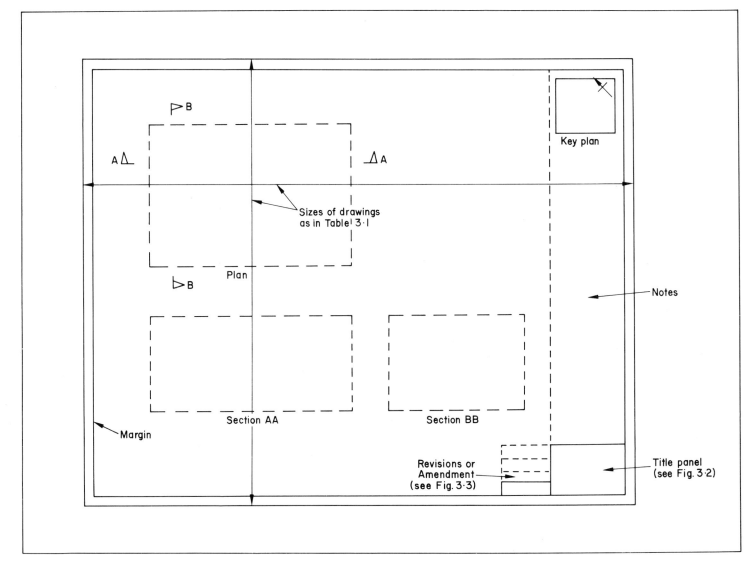

3.1   *General layout of a drawing sheet showing margins, title panel, amendment
block, and the space generally reserved
for notes. With the suggested location
of plan and sections.*

most requirements will be met by the
standard layout shown in Fig. 3.1. This layout is suitable for drawings which will be kept
horizontally in drawers, since the title panels,
etc., can be referred to without having to remove the drawings. You should adopt this layout for all of your exercises, using a simplified
title panel at first.

Drawings can also be filed vertically which
usually saves floor space and gives better
access to each drawing. Some vertical systems have punched suspension strips that are
attached to the drawings so that they can be
hung by their top edge. For this arrangement,
the title panel will have to be at the top of
the drawing so that it can be seen while the
drawing is still in the cabinet. Some vertical
filing systems can store conventionally titled
drawings and still allow the title panel to be
seen.

The standard layout should be maintained
even for 'upright' drawings, that is where the
vertical axis of the drawing is parallel to the
long sides of the sheet.

Most firms standardize their work to two
or three sizes of drawing. It is better to waste
some space on a standard drawing rather than
to be faced with filing an odd sized drawing
which will either slip to the back of a drawer
or be a nuisance in a vertical cabinet. The
draughtsman's time is saved if printed sheets
are used. For routine work, the printing consists of a border and title panel with the name
of the firm or authority. A more complete title
panel should be provided for large schemes
for which many drawings will be made.

**(a) Title panel**

A newcomer to any drawing will need to
assimilate a minimum of information as
quickly as possible before he can interpret

| | |
|---|---|
| (a) Client | **DALESFORD R.D.C.** |
| (b) Scheme | LONGBOTHAM SEWAGE SCHEME |
| (c) Part of scheme | PLAN and SECTIONS of No 3 BOOSTER PUMPING STATION |
| (d) Engineer or consultant | ROBINSON and PARTNERS Chartered Engineers 743 VICTORIA STREET LONDON S.W.I. / *Scales*: 1:100 and 1:50 / *Date*: / *Dwg, No.* 674 C |
| | *Drawn*: T.B.S. / *Checked*: S.B. / *Traced*: C.F.B. |
| | *Approved*: J. Robinson |

*3.2 A typical title panel.*

the drawing. Such information is best presented in the title panel which should always be located in the same place on each drawing.

A cursory glance at a good title panel should tell the observer:

The name of the client or authority for whom the work has been prepared.
The name of the scheme or job.
The part of the job shown on the drawing.
The scales used.
When the drawing was completed.
The name of the engineer or consultant.
The drawing number.

All this information is contained in the title panel shown in Fig. 3.2. Alternative layouts are shown in BS 1192.

The initials of the design engineer are entered in the space marked DRAWN. Civil engineering design, like any design, is open-ended, i.e., there is no single solution. As a result, the chances for errors to creep in are many. It is, therefore, unfair to lay all the responsibility for the design on one man. In an attempt to uncover errors, an independent check of the work must be carried out by another engineer, preferably one who has had little or nothing to do with the detail of the design concerned. His unprejudiced eye will often discover errors or misconceptions that the designer has lived with and overlooked as the design developed. The engineer who carries out the check enters his initials in the CHECKED space.

The ultimate responsibility for the correctness and feasibility of the ideas expressed in the drawing lies with the chief engineer of an authority or a partner in a consultancy. His name will appear in the APPROVED space.

**(b) Revisions or amendments**

Few designs remain unmodified between design and construction. An engineer should never be afraid to amend a design at any stage, if it is necessary to do so. Alterations in the construction phase, however, can be

| DATE | REF. | DETAILS | Draw |
|------|------|---------|------|
|      | C | Intake lowered: pump supports lowered: rising main extended | Ro |
|      | B | Crane details added | 7 |
|      | A | Floor finishes added | |
| | | *Amendments* | |

*3.3   Amendment or revision block showing how it grows upwards.*

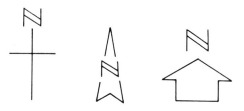

*3.4   Suitable north points.*

very expensive.

Alterations, however small, must be recorded in the revision or amendment panel, which grows upwards, see Fig. 3.3. It is a good idea to incorporate the amendment reference in the drawing number so that superseded drawings can be spotted more easily, e.g., drawing 674C obviously supersedes drawing 674A, etc. The amendments or fresh drawings made on completion of the works to record them 'as built' should have a suitable suffix, R (Record), for example.

**(c)  North points**

The orientation of location and site plans is shown by a north point, see Fig. 3.4.

Use a simple but attractive north point.

**3.4  SCALES**

Drawings for civil engineering range from continental maps with a scale of several millions to one to full-size detail or even larger.

A range of suitable scales and their uses is listed in Table 3.2. The imperial scales they replace are shown alongside.

Table 3.2

| Scale ratio | Use | Previous equivalent |
|-------------|-----|---------------------|
| 1: 50 000 | Location maps | 1 in. to 1 mile 1: 63,360 |
| 1: 10 000 | | 6 in. to 1 mile 1: 10,560 |
| 1: 2500 | Site maps | 1: 2500, about 25 in. to the mile |
| 1. 1250 | | 1: 1250, about 50 in. to the mile |
| 1: 500 | Site plans | |
| 1: 200 | General arrangement | about $\frac{1}{16}$ in. to 1 ft |
| 1: 100 | | about $\frac{1}{8}$ in. to 1 ft |
| 1. 50 | | about $\frac{1}{4}$ in. to 1 ft |
| 1: 25 | Plans, elevations, and sections | about $\frac{1}{2}$ in. to 1 ft |
| 1: 10 | | about 1 in. to 1 ft |
| 1: 5 | Details | about quarter full size |
| 1: 2 | | half full size |
| 1: 1 | | full size |

| Type of line | Example | Application |
|--------------|---------|-------------|
| Continuous (thick) **A** | ——————— | Visible outlines. |
| Continuous (thin) **B** | ——————— | Dimension lines. Projection or extension lines. Hatching or sectioning. Leader lines for notes. Outlines of revolved sections. |
| Short dashes (thin) **C** | - - - - - - | Hidden details. Portions to be removed. |
| Long chain (thin) **D** | — - — - — | Centre lines. Path lines for indicating movement. Pitch circles. |
| Long chain (thick) **E** | — - — - — | Cutting or viewing planes. |
| Short chain (thin) **F** | — - — - — | Developed or false views. Adjacent parts. Feature located in front of a cutting plane. Alternative position of movable part. |
| Continuous wavy (thick) **G** | ~~~~~ | Irregular boundary lines. Short break lines. |
| Ruled line and short zig-zags **H** | —//—//—// | Long break lines. |

*3.5   Types of line.*

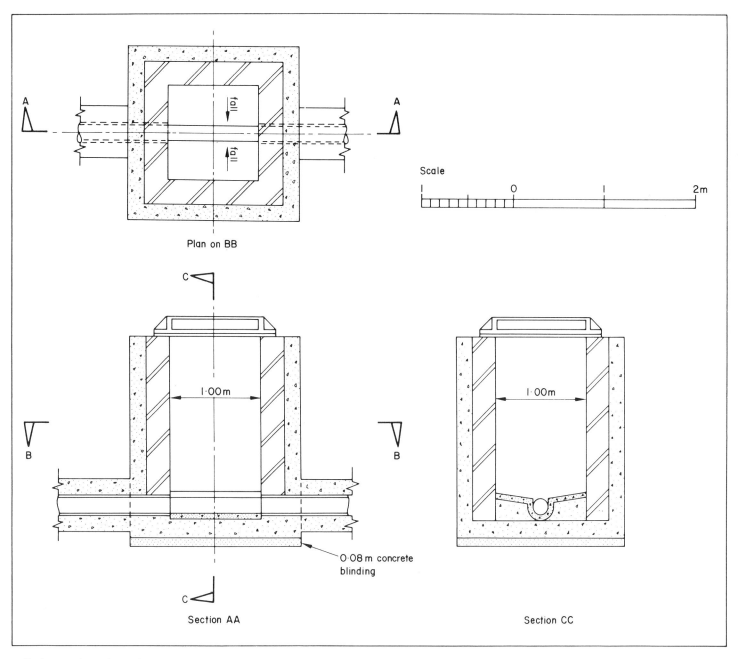

Plan on BB

Scale

Section AA

Section CC

0·08 m concrete blinding

Scales, other than those in Table 3.2, should not be used unless there is a very good reason for doing so. It is better to have a drawing that does not quite fill a standard sheet than to have either a peculiar scale ratio or an odd sized drawing.

It is not usual for dimensions to be scaled from a civil engineering drawing as errors will occur due to paper instability. Probably the only exceptions to this rule are drawings of rough earthworks, when it is useful to include a drawn scale, which will have altered with the paper, see Fig. 3.6 and Fig. 3.10. A drawn scale, and no other, must be used for drawings that will be recorded on microfilm or which may be reduced or enlarged by other photographic means.

### 3.5 TYPES OF LINE

Lines of similar thickness throughout make for a dull drawing, while careful grading of line thickness, with perhaps the skilful use of an extra heavy line here or there, adds interest. This is a good reason for you to start using pens at once for it is difficult to vary the thickness of pencil lines.

The basic types of line are shown in Fig. 3.5.

Lines should be sharp and dense to obtain good reproduction.

3.6 *Arrangement drawing of a small sewerage manhole which shows several types of line, some conventional shading, a drawn scale, and how to reference sections.*

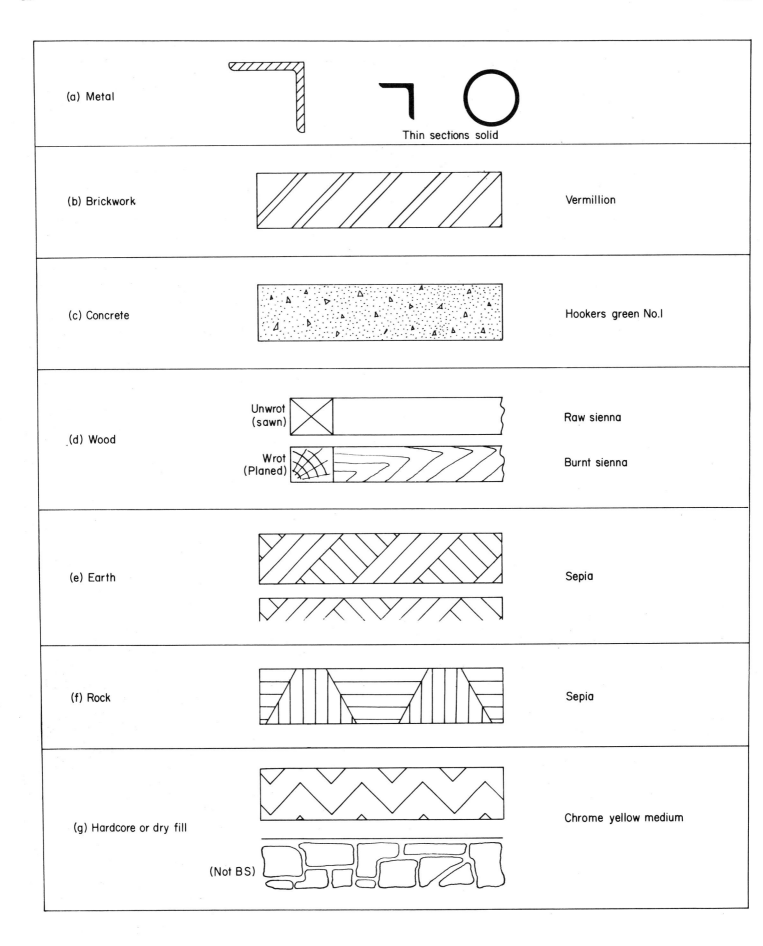

(a) Metal

Thin sections solid

(b) Brickwork — Vermillion

(c) Concrete — Hookers green No.I

(d) Wood

Unwrot (sawn) — Raw sienna

Wrot (Planed) — Burnt sienna

(e) Earth — Sepia

(f) Rock — Sepia

(g) Hardcore or dry fill — Chrome yellow medium

(Not BS)

Lines specified as thick should be from two to three times the thickness of lines specified as thin.

Centre lines should project for a short distance beyond the outline to which they refer, but where necessary to permit dimensioning, they may be extended as dimension lines (Type B). Centre lines should not intersect in the spaces between dashes.

Lines depicting hidden details should always begin and end with a dash in contact with the visible or hidden detail line at which they start or end, except when such a dash would form a continuation or a visible detail line. Dashes should join at corners and arcs should start with dashes at the tangent points. (BS 308)

Various types of line are used in Fig. 3.6 together with some of the sectioning conventions of Fig. 3.7.

## 3.6 SECTIONING
The methods of showing some of the common structural materials when they are exposed in sections are shown in Fig. 3.7.

Although drawings are not often coloured today, a few, carefully chosen, light washes of the conventional colours on a section will enliven the drawing and help the lay observer in his interpretation. The same colour is used for elevational and sectional views of a material, but the section is made darker by the application of a second or third wash after the previous washes have dried.

**Stick-on or rub down shading and other details.**

A variety of special shading effects can be obtained by using self-adhesive or rub down transparent material. It is suitable for placing on tracings, to indicate shading for sections, north points, drawn scales, etc. The use of stick-on or rub down shading speeds the draughting process, while its uniformity creates a more professional effect. Although many of the shading patterns are prepared essentially for commercial artists, the engineer finds some of them useful either on conventional drawings or on cartoons.

It is often more convenient to apply stick-on material to the back of a tracing so that it does not interfere with the linework of the drawing.

Transparent, sensitized, self-adhesive material is available for the preparation of special stick-on shapes. It is a dyeline material, see section 9.4, which can be printed from any negative and is developed conventionally. It has a siliconized backing sheet which is removed to reveal the self-adhesive surface. It is best given a reversed image so that it can be stuck on the back of the tracing. It can be used for standard title panels or, in order to save time, for inserts of maps taken from transparent *Ordnance Survey* sheets.

A selection of rub down sectioning and shading and other details is shown in Fig. 3.8.

## 3.7 DIMENSIONS AND LEVELS
A particular form of dimension met in civil engineering is the level, i.e., the height of a point above a chosen datum which is usually the *Ordnance Survey* datum, but can be any convenient reference. Levels replace vertical dimensions on drawings which leads to simplification.

Figure 3.9 (a) shows the system of dimensions suggested in BS 308 which is applicable to civil engineering practice.

The nature of civil engineering work allows most dimensions to be given in multiples of 10 mm, i.e., 10.47 1045.00 or 0.76 in metres. If the scale of the drawing or the resolution require it, dimensions can be given in millimetres i.e., 765, 1574 or 5. The presence of the decimal point will indicate whether the units are metres or millimetres. Dimensions must be consistent on a drawing, wholly in metres or millimetres, not mixed. An occasional dimension shown with a resolution closer than 10 mm, say 10.473, will draw attention to a particular need for greater accuracy. Levels can comfortably be read to 5 mm, i.e., 104.675; accuracy closer than this is often wishful thinking.

Figure 3.9 (b) shows some frequently used alternatives to the arrowheads used in (a). Arrowheads should be slim, say 5° each side of the shaft, and can be filled in or left hollow.

Dimensions can sit on the dimension line or be let into it. The two systems should not be mixed in one drawing. Dimensions on a vertical dimension line should have their base to the right, the natural way a right-handed draughtsman would write them. The left-hander will either have to remove the drawing from the board and twist it into a comfortable position or walk round the board, if he can, to print the figures.

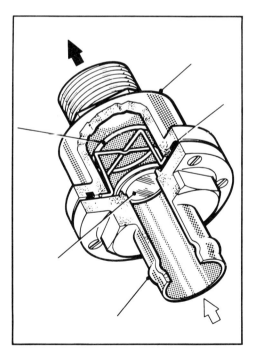

3.7 *Conventional shading and colours for some constructional materials (BS 1192).*

3.8 *Examples of some rub down symbols and shading (some are special orders). (Photograph supplied by Letraset Limited.)*

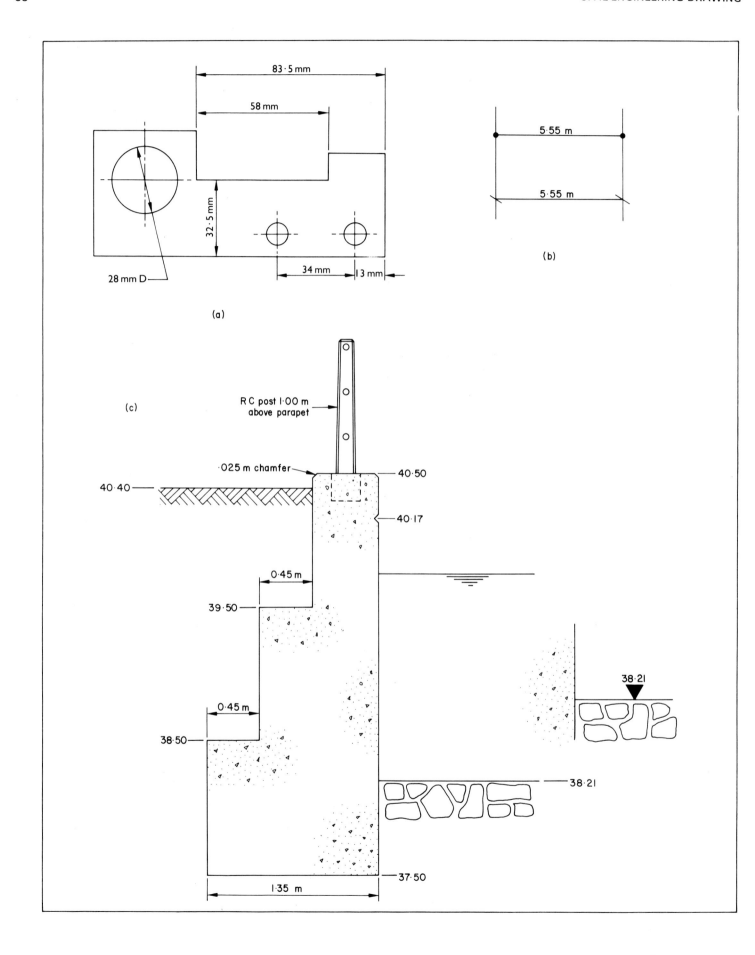

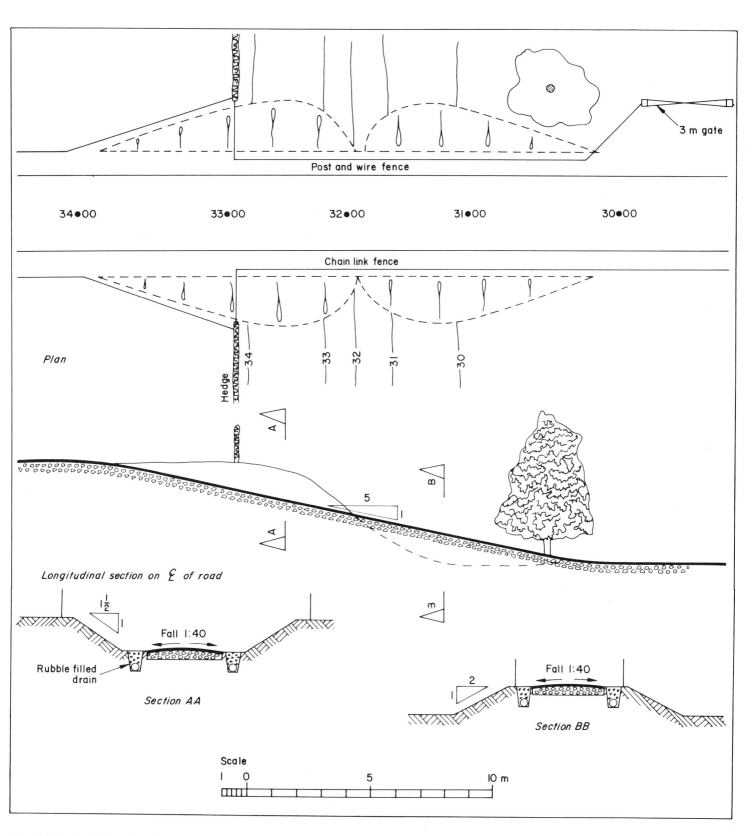

3 m gate

Post and wire fence

34●00    33●00    32●00    31●00    30●00

Chain link fence

*Plan*

Hedge

A

B

5

A

*Longitudinal section on ₵ of road*

$1\frac{1}{2}$

1

Fall 1:40

Rubble filled drain

*Section AA*

B

Fall 1:40

2

1

*Section BB*

Scale

1  0          5          10 m

3.9  *Methods of showing dimensions.*

(a) *From BS 308.*

(b) *Alternatives sometimes used for arrowheads.*

(c) *Two methods of showing levels.*

3.10  *Simple earthworks with several methods of showing slopes, contours, hatching (tadpoles), spot levels, etc.*

Figure 3.9 (c) shows a suitable system of dimensioning for civil engineering work. A shaded triangle to indicate levels is acceptable when a leader line cannot conveniently be taken to a clear part of the drawing, e.g., invert and soffit levels. (The invert of a pipe or tunnel is the bottom where the water flows, the soffit is the underside of the roof.)

The level of a flat area in a plan, a concrete deck, for example, is shown in a rectangular box, e.g., $\boxed{37.35}$  Some authorities also suggest boxing the values of levels in sections and elevations as well. A spot level on a road or in a field is shown as a dot, with the value written beside it. It is often convenient to use the decimal point of the level as the dot, see Fig. 3.10.

A contour line, which is a line in the plan joining points of the same altitude and usually restricted to natural slopes, is also shown in Fig. 3.10.

## 3.8 SLOPES, FALLS, BATTERS, AND GRADIENTS

These are all words the engineer uses (sometimes indiscriminately) for a slope.

Batters are usually the steep faces of embankments or cuttings, see Fig. 3.10, while gradients are the less severe slopes of roads or railways.

Fairly steep slopes are shown in the plan by tadpoles which swim uphill, while flatter slopes are shown by contour lines. Tadpoles are usually restricted to artificial slopes the limits of which can be shown by dotted lines.

## 3.9 LETTERING

Many good drawings are ruined by poor printing.

You should aim at a simple style that can be executed quickly freehand, see Fig. 3.11 (b).

Do not make the letters too big.

Use a slightly softer pencil which is not too sharp.

Few of us can make a really neat job of letters much more than 10 mm high, so it is sometimes worthwhile using letter stencils for titles, but this is very slow. For prestige work, the very professional effect obtained by stick-down letters such as *Letraset*, *Presletta*, etc., is worth the extra time and effort involved, see Fig. 3.11 (c).

(a)

(b)

(c)

3.11  *Some examples of printing.*
   *(a) Stencil.*
   *(b) Freehand.*
   *(c) Self-adhesive transfers. (Photograph supplied by Letraset Limited.)*

Precise, true-to-standard lettering and symbols, using drawing pens, can be obtained with the Rotring NC-scriber, see Fig. 3.12.

With the help of microprocessors, all plotting operations are performed by program control; the interchangeable drawing pens are guided with utmost precision in vertical and horizontal steps.

The standard program of the NC-scriber embraces altogether 140 characters, digits and symbols which can be called in by operating keys.

Characters and symbols between 1 mm and 30 mm in size can be pre-set in increments of 0.1 mm via a keyboard entry.

The NC-scriber consists of a functional unit, designed to fit on to the drawing head of a draughting machine.

## 3.10 TEMPLATES

Templates are available to speed up the work in drawing standard units and symbols. They cover an exceptionally wide range of subjects. An RIBA Architectural Template is illustrated in Fig. 3.13.

Lettering templates for use with pen or pencil are also produced and these provide a cheaper method of preparing standard letters and figures than using the rub-down letter sheets mentioned previously.

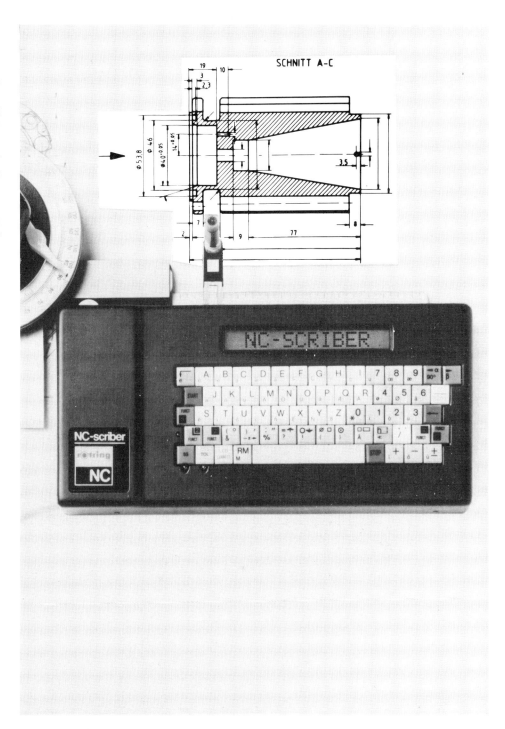

*3.12 Rotring NC-scriber fitted to the drawing head of a draughting machine. (U.K. distributors: Hartley Reece & Company, Wembley, Middx.)*

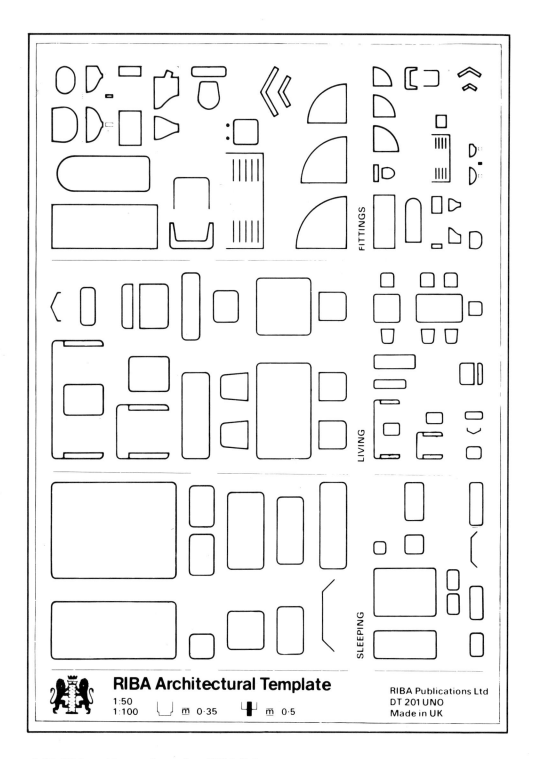

3.13 RIBA architectural template (RIBA Pub-
lications Ltd, DT 201 UNO)

Part Two            Geometry

Chapter 4           Points, lines, surfaces,
                    and shadows

*Towing an oil platform to the North sea fields.*
*(Photograph supplied by the New Civil Engineer)*

## 4.1 INTRODUCTION

The engineer can conveniently divide the surfaces of three-dimensional shapes into two groups, those which can be developed precisely and those which cannot.

A surface is said to be developed when it is laid out flat. For example, the faces of the cube on to which the orthographic views in Chapter 2 are projected are developed in Fig. 2.4, although only three of the six faces are shown. The resulting flat shape is called the development of the surface.

Plane or singly curved surfaces (see definitions below) can be developed exactly, whereas doubly curved or warped surfaces can be developed only approximately.

Figures 4.1 and 4.3 show how several different surfaces are formed by a moving line called a generator. Any position of the generator is an element of the surfaces.

A plane surface is generated, see Fig. 4.1 (a), by a straight line AB moving in a straight line while remaining parallel to its original position. A′ B′ is an element of the surface.

A singly curved surface is generated, see Fig. 4.1 (b), by a straight line moving so that adjacent positions lie in the same plane, e.g., in (bi) A′ B′ A″ B″ lie in the same plane as AB′ AB″ in (bii).

Adjacent positions of the generator of warped surfaces, see Fig. 4.1 (c), do not lie in the same plane. They cannot be developed. Three common examples of warped surfaces are shown.

(ci) A smooth transition between trapezoidal and rectangular channels.

(cii) A parabolic hyperboloid in which the stiffness of a doubly curved structure is achieved with straight elements A′ B′.

(ciii) A circular hyperboloid whose generation is best understood by imagining straight elements attached to circular plates top and bottom which are then rotated relative to each other, 90° in this case.

Although (cii) is often known as an hyperbolic paraboloid, it is better to think of all warped surfaces which have the hyperbola as the main contour as hyperboloids. Sections other than the main one will reveal other conic sections, see Chapter 5, which classify the shape within the hyperboloid family. The cooling tower or circular hyperboloid in (ciii) has circular horizontal sections.

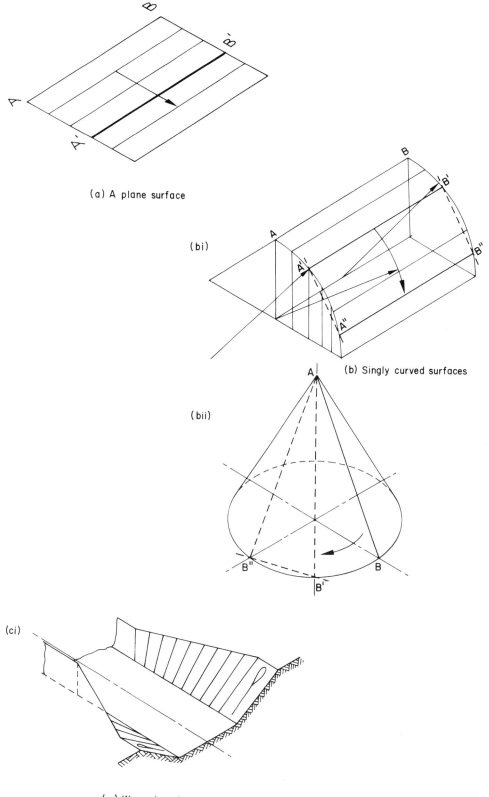

(a) A plane surface

(bi)

(b) Singly curved surfaces

(bii)

(ci)

(c) Warped surfaces

4.1 Generation of surfaces.
(a) Plane surface by a straight line.
(b) Singly curved surfaces by a straight line.
(c) Warped surfaces by straight lines.

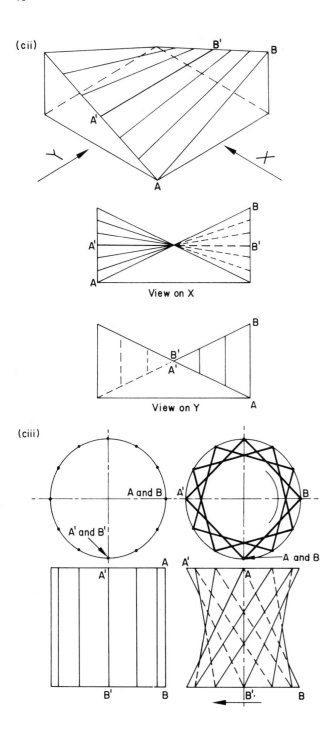

(cii)

A'

B'

B

View on X

A'

B'

B

View on Y

A

(ciii)

A and B

A' and B'

A'

B

A and B

A'

A

B'

B

B'

B

*4.2 Construction of an hyperboloid showing elements touching all three directrices, AB, CD, and EF, with an additional element passing through point X on CD.*

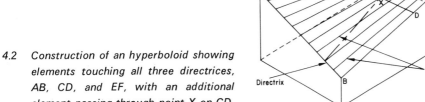

The Americans refer to hyperboloids as double-ruled surfaces because two elements can pass through certain points on their surface.

An hyperboloid is defined, see Fig. 4.2, by three nonparallel directrices, AB, CD, and EF, that do not intersect. The surface is generated by elements that touch all three directrices, the lines that direct or determine the shape.

The circular hyperboloid has circular directrices, one at the top, one at the bottom, and the waist or gore circle. Two different elements can cross on the middle directrix.

If smooth warped surfaces are to be built in concrete, the shuttering can be made of planking laid parallel to the elements of the surface with a minimum of twist in each board. While the necessary cables, if prestressed concrete is being used, can be straight with consequent easing of the tensioning process.

It is sometimes convenient to imagine that a singly curved surface is generated by a curved line moving in a straight path, see Fig. 4.3 (a).

Doubly curved surfaces are generated, see Fig. 4.3 (b), by curved lines moving on curved paths, at a radius R (bi) or about its own axis (bii).

**4.2 LINES IN AN ENGINEERING DRAWING**
Lines in an engineering drawing represent:
(a) The edge view of a plane.
(b) The intersection of two planes.
(c) The horizon of a curved surface.

Compare the orthographic view in Fig. 4.4 with the isometric one while considering (a), (b), and (c) above.
(a) The line CA represents the edge of the plane CAJG.
(b) The line BA represents the intersection of planes BAC and BAD.
(c) The line EH represents the horizon of the curved upper block when seen in the direction of the arrow X, and also the edge of the plane EFGH. Note that there is no line PQ as there is no sharp edge there.

The single orthographic view in Fig. 4.4 does not fully describe the shape of the block since there is no indication of the curved surface. A view in the direction of the arrow Y would show the curvature, but there could be doubt about the fillet.

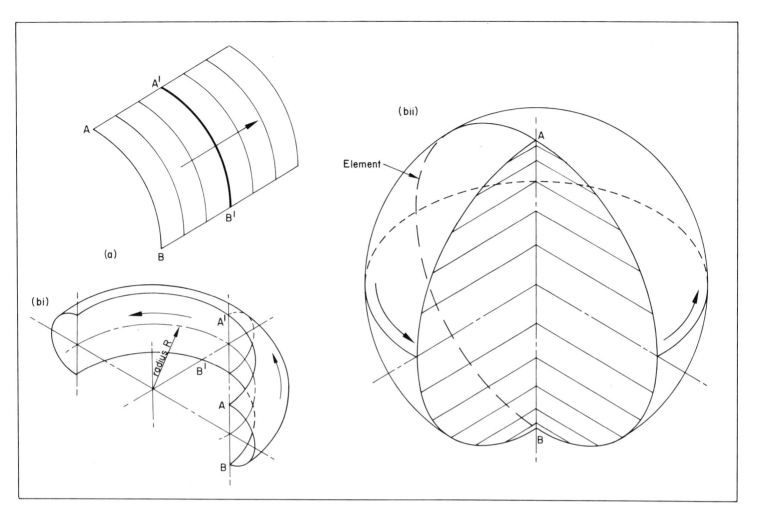

4.3 Generation of surfaces.
   (a) Singly curved surface by a curved line.
   (b) Doubly curved surfaces by a curved line.

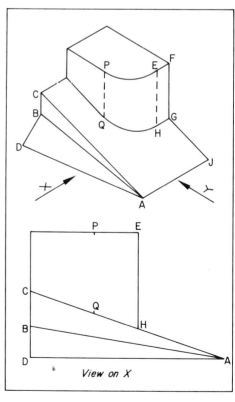

4.4 Use of lines in engineering drawing to show.
   (a) The edge of a plane—line CA.
   (b) The intersection of two planes—line BA.
   (c) The horizon of a curved surface—line EH.

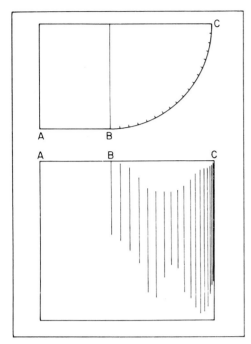

Sometimes, the impression of a curved surface can be given nonconventionally by light shading. In Fig. 4.5, equally spaced points located round the curve in the plan, when dropped into the elevation, become closer from B to C thereby inferring a curved surface bending into (or out of) the plane of the paper.

*4.5 Showing curved surfaces nonconventionally.*

## 4.3 DESCRIPTIVE GEOMETRY

Descriptive geometry is the graphical solution of problems concerned with points, lines, and surfaces in three dimensions and is intimately concerned with engineering drawing and projection.

### (a) Lines

Figure 4.6(i) (a) is a three-dimensional view

*4.6(i)  Line AB on the sloping face of a wedge.*
*(a) Three-dimensionally.*
*(b) Orthographically with auxiliary section to find the true length and inclination of AB.*

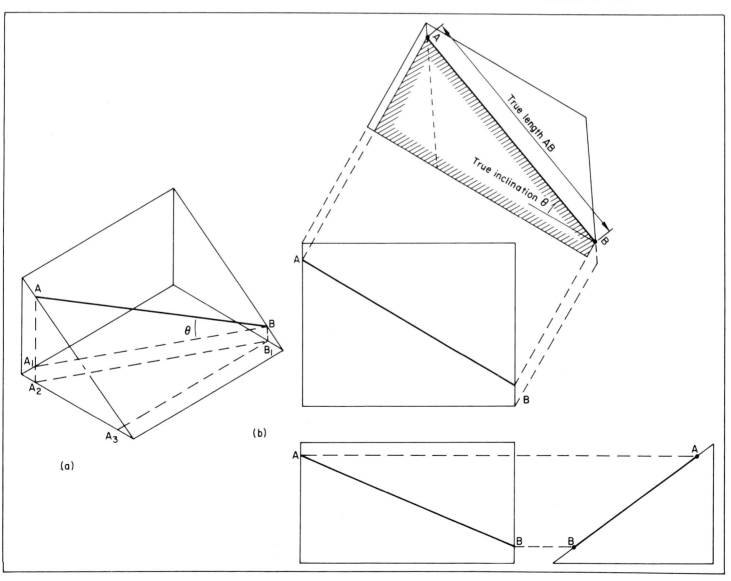

of a line AB on the sloping face of a wedge. AB is inclined to all three planes of projection.

The first step is usually to find the true length of the given line and its inclination to the horizontal.

This can be done analytically from the co-ordinates of points A and B using Pythagoras' theorem to find in turn the length of the hypotenuse $A_2B_1$ of triangle $B_1A_3A_2$ and then AB from triangle $AA_1B$. As all the sides of triangle $AA_1B$ are known, the angle $\theta$ can be found.

Figure 4.6(i) (b) shows three orthographic views of the wedge with the line AB, which is foreshortened in each view. An auxiliary view is necessary, projected on to a plane parallel to the line AB in the plan, to show the true length of AB and its inclination $\theta$ to the horizontal.

The centre line of a road, with a constant gradient, climbing up the side of a valley, is an application of a line on an inclined plane. With contour lines 5 m apart, as shown in Fig. 4.7, and a road gradient of 1 vertical in 10 horizontal, successive points, 5 m apart vertically, will have a horizontal separation of 50 m. Starting at A, with dividers set to 50 m, points can be located on successive contour lines by walking the dividers up the slope. As the gradient is so flat (geometrically speaking, although it is sufficient to slow down heavy vehicles), the true length of the road is almost the same as its plan length; each 50 m horizontal intercept represents a piece of road $50 \times \sqrt{\dfrac{101}{100}}$ m long.

Another problem encountered by the civil engineer is the relative positions of objects, for example two pipes which may or may not intercept. The answer can be found by drawing an auxiliary view or views of the pipes which will eventually show one of them as an end view or a single point. Figure 4.6(ii) shows the plan and elevation of two pipes or lines.

As in Fig. 4.6(i), determine the true length of one of the lines, in this case C-D. Look along this true length line and show the line as a point. The clearance is the shortest distance between this point and projected view of the other line.

**(b) Planes**

Figure 4.8 shows how an infinite plane can be defined by three points A, B, and C.

The determination of the true slope of a plane is an essential exercise in geology where the plane is represented by a plane stratum of rock and the true slope is known

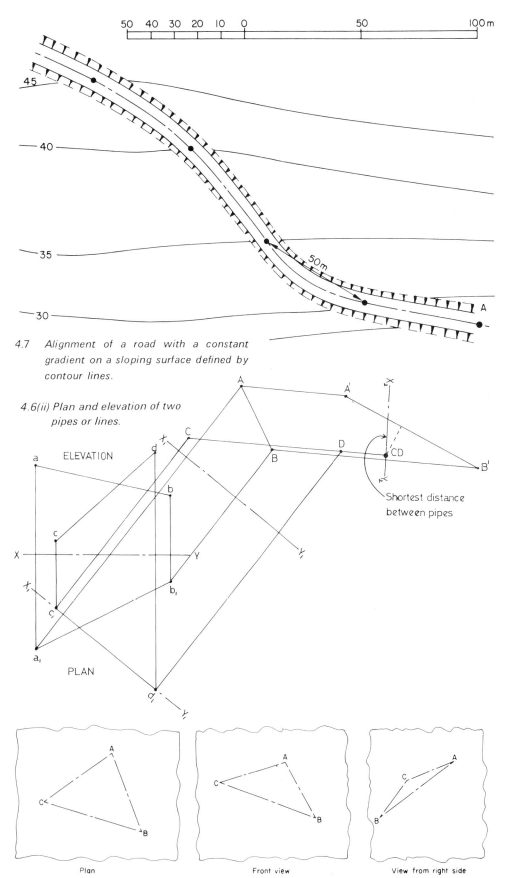

4.7 Alignment of a road with a constant gradient on a sloping surface defined by contour lines.

4.6(ii) Plan and elevation of two pipes or lines.

4.8 Orthographic views of an inclined infinite plane defined by the three points, A, B, and C.

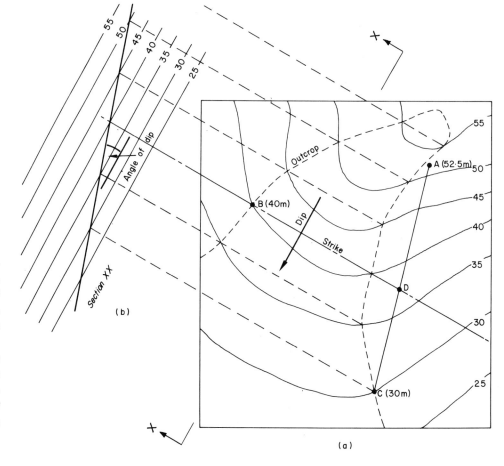

4.9   (a) Contour map of three outcrops, A,
          B, and C, of the same rock stratum,
          showing location of D at same level
          as B to define the strike. The in-
          ferred shape of the outcrop is also
          shown.
      (b) Section XX taken at right angles to
          the strike to show the dip or true
          slope of the stratum, with construc-
          tion lines for determining points of
          the outcrop on contour lines in the
          map.

as the dip of the stratum.

Figure 4.9 (a) is a contoured map showing three outcrops of rock A, B, and C, which are known to be on top of the same plane stratum of rock. First find the strike of the stratum, which is the bearing of a horizontal line on its surface, by finding the point D in AC which lies at the same level as B, by dividing AC proportionately. The dip lies at right angles to the strike. Its value can be found graphically by drawing the section XX, see Fig. 4.9 (b), as an auxiliary view on a plane parallel to the dip.

Once the dip is known, the shape of the outcrop can be found on the map. Points on the outcrop are located graphically where lines from the section, projected parallel to the strike, intersect contour lines with the same level.

## 4.4 DEVELOPMENTS

A surface is said to be developed when it has been laid out flat; the resulting flat shape is called the development of the surface.

The civil engineer may become involved with ducting for ventilation or with fabricated pipes and tunnels for hydraulic schemes. Although he may not be concerned with the fabrication of pipes, a knowledge of what is or what is not readily developable will result in a better, cheaper job for his client.

Most civil engineers, however, will be concerned with shuttering for concrete at some time in their careers, and for this, a knowledge of development techniques is essential, either in the design and erection of the shuttering or in choosing seemingly complicated shapes that can be shuttered simply.

Developments are closely connected with intersections, see section 4.5. Both are exercises in finding the true length of lines in space inclined to the orthographic axes.

### (a) Development of a right circular cone

Figure 4.10 shows the plan, elevations, and development of a right circular cone. A singly curved and, therefore, developable surface which is created by the movement of the generator OG so that O remains fixed while G describes a circle. Its instantaneous position OG is an element of the cone.

The development of the cone is a segment

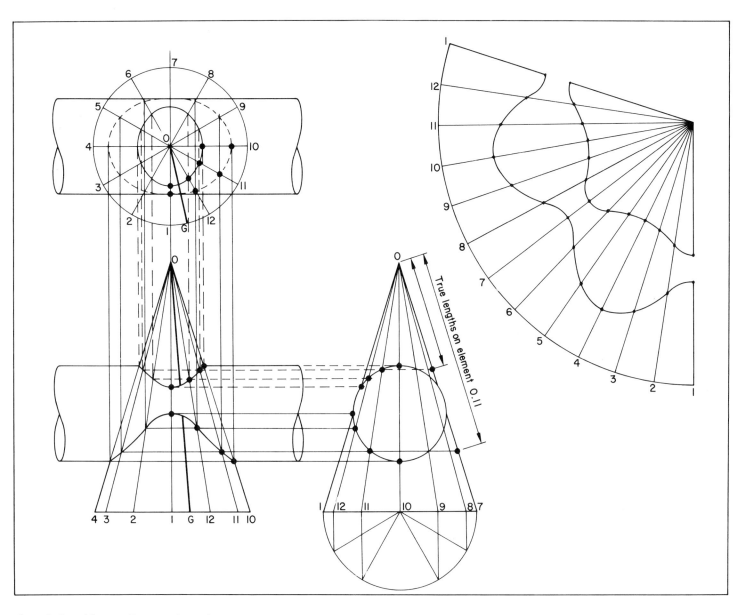

of a circle with a radius equal to the true length of the generator and a peripheral length equal to the length of the path traced by G in the plan. In Fig. 4.10 the length 1.1 in the development is twelve steps of the chord between adjacent numbered points in the plan. It is convenient to use a 'sixty thirty' set square to divide the plan. In full size work, the periphery of the development would be calculated accurately and then be set out carefully on the curve.

The elemental method of developing a cone can very quickly solve problems of penetration of the cone by other geometric shapes, such as by the cylinder in Fig. 4.10.

The heavily marked intersections of the cylinder with the numbered elements of the cone in the side elevation are projected into the

front elevation and, then, up into the plan. Both front elevation and plan can then be completed.

The true length of the generator OG appears only at O.4 and O.10 in the front elevation and at O.1 and O.7 in the side elevation. Thus true distances of the intersection points from the apex of the cone, required for construction of the development, are found by projecting the intersection points horizontally to the line O.7 in the side elevation, or using the intercepts on lines O.1 in the side elevation or on O.10 in the front view.

**(b)  Development of an oblique circular cone**

An oblique circular cone is shown in Fig. 4.11. It has a circular base to which its axis is inclined.

The true length of all the elements must be

*4.10  Development, by use of elements, of a right circular cone penetrated by a cylinder.*

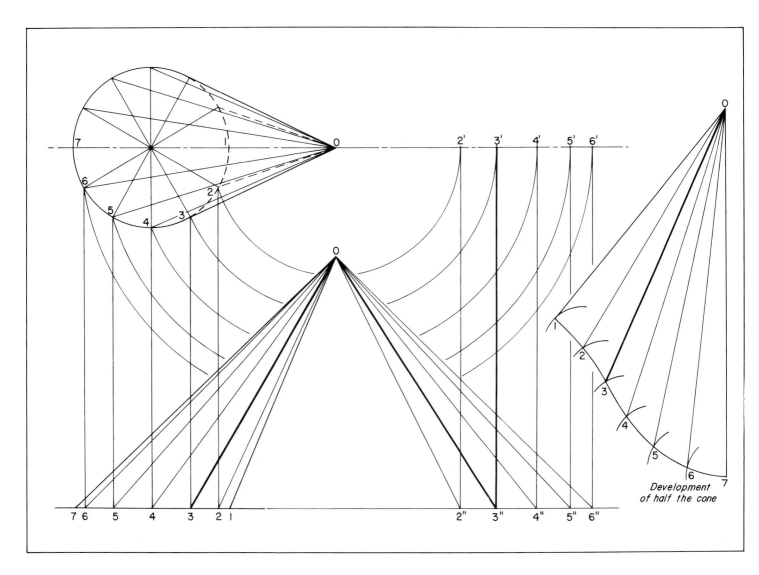

4.11 *Development, by use of elements, of an oblique cone.*

found. O.1 and O.7 alone show their true lengths in the elevation. The horizontal projection of the elements appears in the plan. The elements have a common vertical projection, the height of the cone. The true length of an element will be the hypotenuse of a right-angled triangle incorporating its two projections.

Consider element O.3:
(a) Centre O, radius O.3 in the plan, swing an arc to cut the centre line produced at 3'.
(b) Drop a vertical from 3' to meet the base of the elevation produced at 3''.
(c) The true length of O.3 appears as O.3'' in the elevation.

To complete the development:
(d) Set up O.7, taken directly from the elevation.
(e) Centre 7, radius equal to the chord 6.7, swing an arc.

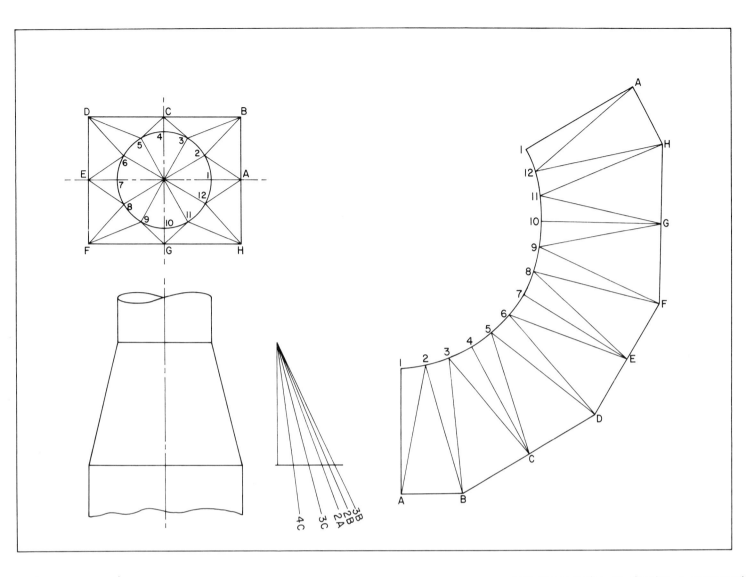

(f) Centre O, radius 0.6", swing an arc to cut the previous arc at 6.

### (c) Development of compound shapes

All shapes, whether regular or not, can be developed by the true length element method of triangulation used for the oblique cone in section 4.4 (b).

This method is applied to the transition between a circular duct and a rectangular one in Fig. 4.12.

The chosen section lines or elements which triangulate the transition must pass through salient points, e.g., the corners of the rectangular duct. In the plan, the periphery of the circular duct is divided by radial lines 30° apart. The true lengths of the elements in the quadrant ABC are found in the separate construction; they have a common height and their horizontal projections are transferred from the plan.

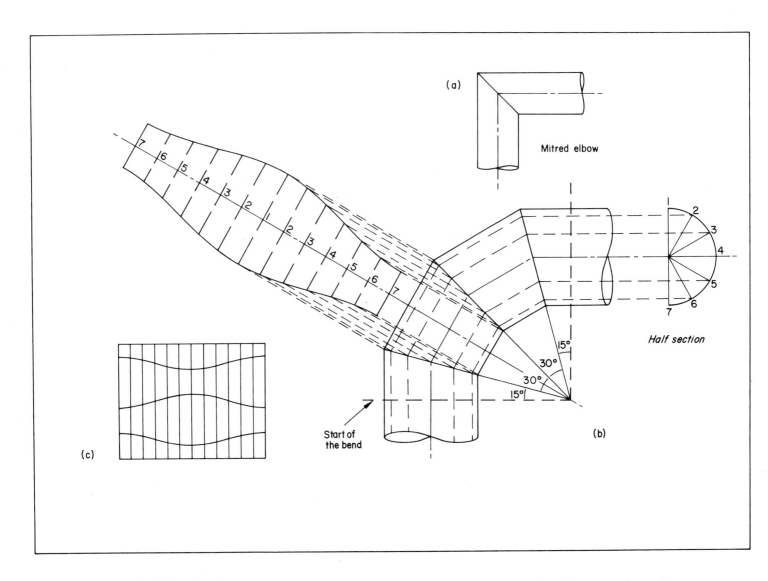

4.13 Development of bends in a pipe showing the 'lobster backed' elements and how they can be cut with little waste.

(a) A mitred elbow.

(b) Development of one element, a 'lobster backed' plate.

(c) The four elements developed economically on one sheet.

**(d) Development of bends in pipes or tunnels**

The simple mitred elbow shown in Fig. 4.13 (a) is very bad hydraulically. A bend made up of two or more segments, however, as shown in (b), is almost as good as a smooth one made of doubly curved surfaces, but it is much easier to make and, therefore, cheaper.

The problem is to find true lengths that can be set out on a plane to construct the development. In this case, the symmetrical development can be defined by two dimensions at right angles without the need for triangulation. The two dimensions are round the periphery of the pipe and along its axis. The former appear in the half section as the chords 12, 23, 34, etc., and the latter appear directly on the plan as the dotted lines constructed from the points 1, 2, 3, etc., on the section.

While the shape of the elements of the bend is best understood as they are developed

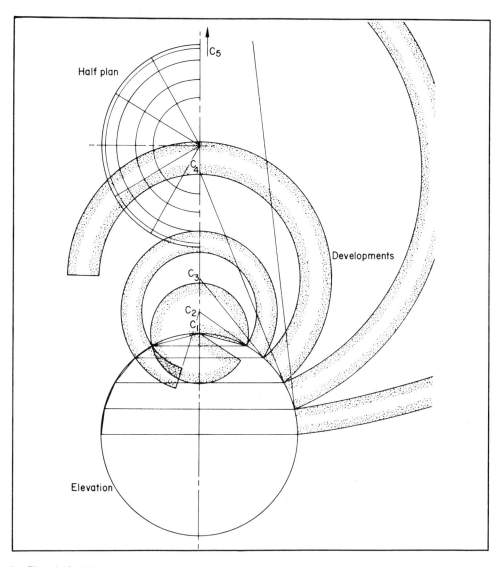

*4.14 Approximate development of a doubly curved surface—frustra of cones.*

in Fig. 4.13 (b), considerable economy of material and cutting will result from the re-arrangement of the pieces as shown in (c). Moreover greater strength will result after assembly since the longitudinal welds are staggered.

Note that as the ellipses at the end of each completed element must be identical, the first join is made 15° after the start of the bend.

### (e) Approximate developments of doubly curved surfaces

The following treatment of the sphere should enable you to devise approximations of other doubly curved shapes.

In Fig. 4.14 the elevation of the sphere is divided into a number of horizontal slices thus creating a conical cap and a number of elemental frustra. Note that each frustum is from a right circular cone of different apex angle and will give rise to circular elements

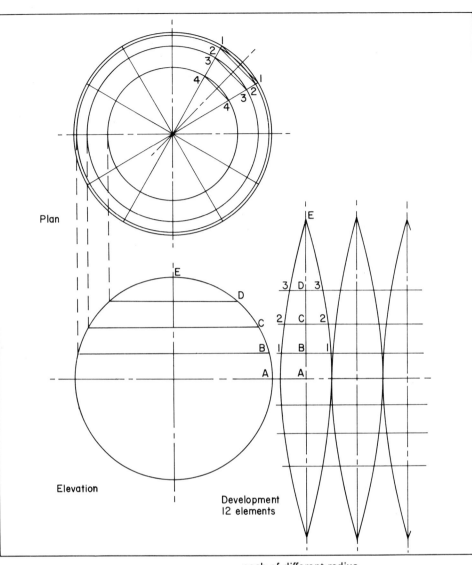

Plan

Elevation

Development
12 elements

4.15 *Approximate development of a doubly curved surface—segments.*

each of different radius.

Each element can be drawn precisely, but much material is wasted in cutting each one out.

In Fig. 4.15 the elevation is divided into a number of slices and the plan into a number of equal segments. The peripheral lengths of the slices AB, BC, etc., in the elevation represent the lengths of the elements, while the plan lengths 11, 22, 33, represent the widths.

The elements are similar and so can be produced economically in a series.

### 4.5 INTERSECTIONS (interpenetrations)

An intersection is the junction between geometric shapes, e.g., a hole punched in a card is the intersection of a plane and a cylinder.

While precise developments are limited to plane and singly curved surfaces, orthographic views of intersections of doubly curved sur-

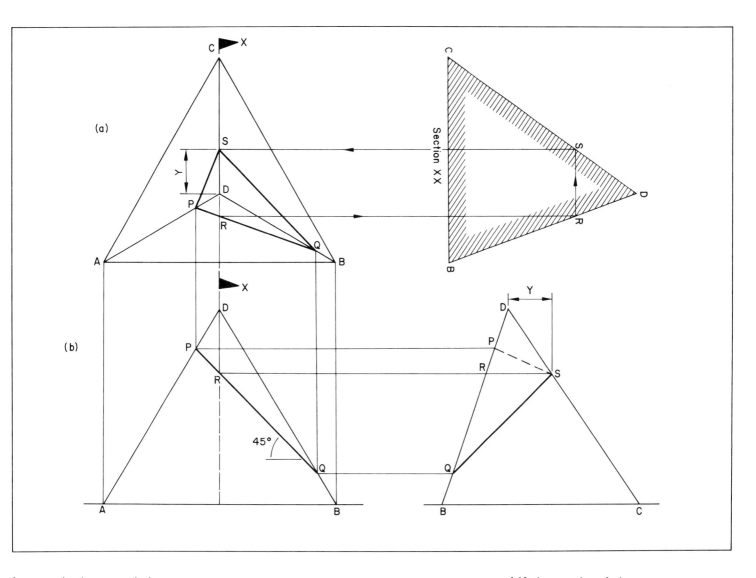

4.16 Intersection of planes.
(a) To form a pyramid.
(b) To intersect the pyramid.

faces can be drawn precisely.

An extended study of a particular intersection that of a plane with a right circular cone, is made in Chapter 5.

The intersections studied in this chapter range from planes to singly and doubly curved surfaces.

The problem is one of locating a point in space, usually by finding sections of two or more orthographic views that contain the same point.

**(a) Intersection of planes**

A pyramid is formed by the intersection of planes. The orthographic views of a tetrahedron, Fig. 4.16, show the straight lines that result from planes intersecting symmetrically.

You should attempt to draw the three orthographic views of this deceptively simple figure before moving on to more advanced intersections.

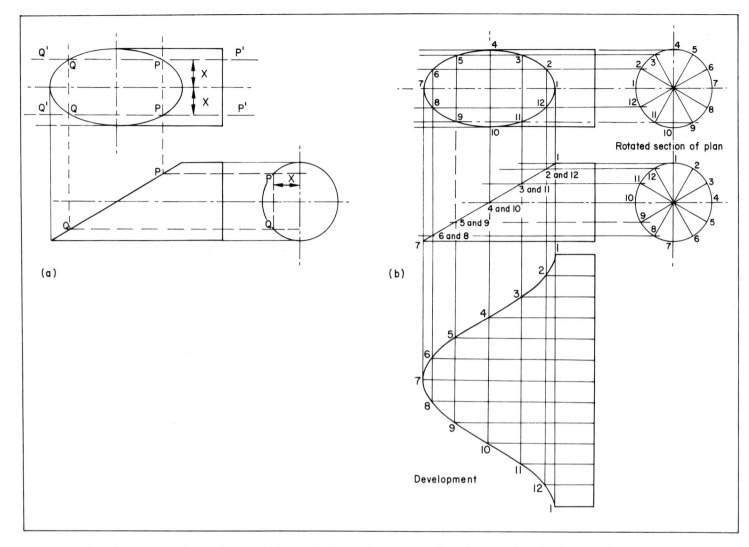

*4.17  Intersection of a plane with a cylinder with its development.*

The thicker lines show another plane intersecting the tetrahedron asymmetrically. This plane, PQ, is at 45° to the base, as shown in the front view. The line RS is horizontal.

The points P and Q can be projected directly into the plan and the side elevation. If the point R is projected into the section XX, the location of S on the rear edge CD can be found and projected back into the plan. Alternatively, the point S can be found in the side elevation (on the same level as R) and the dimension Y can be transferred to the plan.

**(b) Intersection of a plane with a cylinder**

In Fig. 4.17 the two front elevations show that the end of the cylinder has been cut at an angle, i.e., it has been intersected by a plane.

The plan view of the cut end is built up by taking a number of sections and showing them in both views and also in the end elevation.

In Fig. 4.17 (a) the point P is located any-

where in the elevation, and is projected into the plan and the end view. The dimension X must be transferred to the plan from the end view.

The symmetrical location of sections shown in Fig. 4.17 (b) is better. The end elevation and a rotated section of the plan are divided radially (say at 30° intervals). These section lines are carefully referenced. In this example, points 1 and 7 lie at the top and bottom of the cylinder respectively. You should project lines into the elevation to locate points systematically on the intersecting plane, and label them. Then, create verticals from these points into the plan to intersect horizontals from the rotated section. Points in the plan are located at the intersection of lines with the same reference.

The development of the cut cylinder appears almost as a byproduct of this exercise. Again, the arc is approximated to the chord between adjacent numbers on the periphery of the

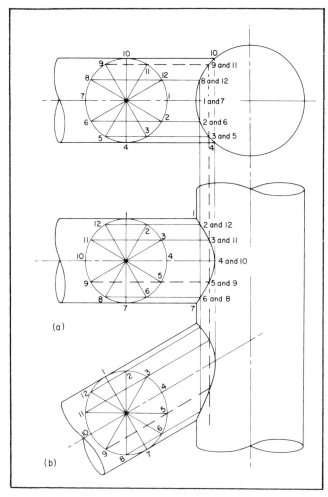

*4.18 Intersection of cylinders.*

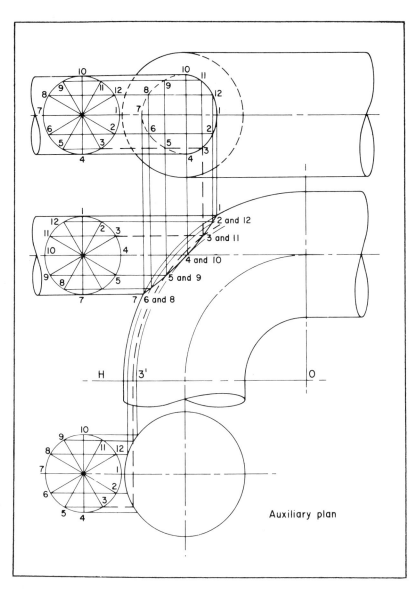

cylinder.

### (c) Intersection of cylinders

In the arrangement shown in Fig. 4.18, the plan view can be completed at once, but the elevation must be built up. In (a) the branch cylinder is normal to the main one, whereas it is inclined, or oblique, in (b).

Again a symmetrical radial division of the intersecting cylinder is used in plan and elevation with each point being given the same reference in each view. Note that rotated sections are used instead of end views for the radial division and reference numbers.

Now project lines from any reference, say 9, into both views (heavy dotted lines). From the intersection of one of these lines with the intersecting surface in the plan, drop a vertical to intersect the other line in the elevation to establish the point 9 on the intersection.

In Fig. 4.19 a variation of the same theme is shown, the intersection of a straight cylinder with a curved one.

Neither plan nor elevation can be completed without some construction.

(a) Draw an auxiliary plan of the smaller cylinder intersecting a vertical section of the larger one. Use the symmetrical radial division of rotated sections in all three views, plan, elevation, and auxiliary plan, and number similar points.

(b) Project horizontals from the same reference 3, in all three views.

(c) From the intersection of one of these horizontals with the cutting face (the larger cylinder) in the auxiliary plan, erect a vertical to meet the horizontal OH at 3' in the elevation. OH is the start of the bend.

(d) Swing an arc, radius 03', to cut the horizontal from reference 3 in the elevation and locate the point on the inter-

*4.19 Intersection of a straight cylinder with a curved one.*

section.

(e) Erect a vertical from this point in the elevation to intersect the third horizontal in the plan to locate point 3 therein.

CIVIL ENGINEERING DRAWING

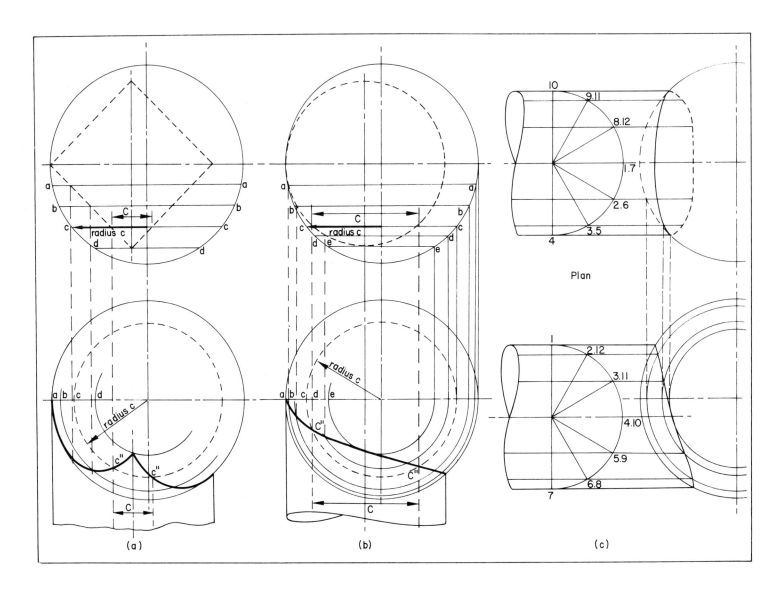

4.20 *Intersection of a sphere with plane and curved surfaces.*

**(d) Intersection of planes and cylinders with a sphere**

Sometimes the intersection of a doubly curved surface with a plane or other surfaces can be surprisingly simple. This is illustrated by Fig. 4.20 (a) which depicts a sphere sitting on a square base and Fig. 4.20 (b) which depicts a sphere sitting on a cylindrical base.

As in the previous examples, the construction can best be understood if sections are taken through both the intersecting shapes on the same plane. In examples (a) and (b), a vertical section CC, as defined on the plan, is taken.

At section CC, the sphere has a radius c and the base tube is C wide. The section shown in heavy dotted lines in the elevation would result if the assembly were to be cut on CC. The two points, C″, where the sections of the sphere and the base tubes intersect, lie on the intersection being constructed.

The construction points on the intersections are fairly evenly spaced. While, in the plan, cross sections are crammed together towards the outer limits of the cylindrical base. Do not start constructions with too many points. In this case, four sections were used initially for both examples. This proved to be enough for the square base. Extra points were provided for the cylindrical base. Their location was determined by the requirements of the construction of the intersection in the elevation.

In (c) the sections are shown related to the familiar symmetrical radial division of the intersecting cylinder in both the plan and elevation. The same references apply.

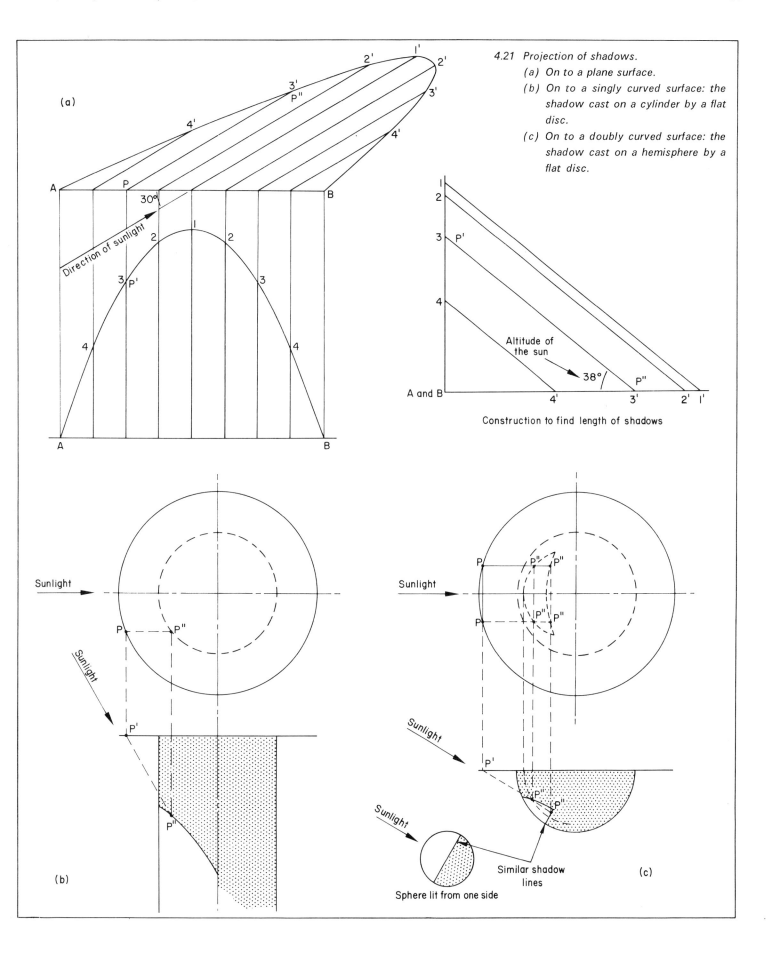

(a)

Direction of sunlight

30°

Construction to find length of shadows

Altitude of the sun

38°

4.21 Projection of shadows.

(a) On to a plane surface.

(b) On to a singly curved surface: the shadow cast on a cylinder by a flat disc.

(c) On to a doubly curved surface: the shadow cast on a hemisphere by a flat disc.

Sunlight

(b)

Sunlight

Sphere lit from one side

Similar shadow lines

(c)

## 4.6 SHADOWS

Although engineers do not usually show shadows on their drawings to give depth or roundness to elevations, a study of the projection of shadows is a useful extension of three-dimensional thinking and some help in visualization.

If sunlight projects a shadow at right angles on to a plane surface, the shadow is an orthographic silhouette of the elevation presented to the plane, like the silhouette 'portraits' which were popular in the nineteenth century. Usually however the rays of light fall obliquely on to a plane or even a curved surface with consequent distortion of the shadow. Our own long shadows, cast by the setting sun, are a familiar example of this.

Three simple examples of shadow projections appear in Fig. 4.21 where shadows are cast on both flat and curved surfaces.

The three-dimensional problem involving the horizontal and vertical angles of the rays of the sun can be reduced to two dimensions. This is done by basing the construction, for finding the length of the cast shadows, on an axis determined by the horizontal angle of the sun's rays. In Fig. 4.21 (a) where the sunlight strikes the parabolic arch asymmetrically, the length of the shadows is determined on an auxiliary plane, whereas the symmetry of the objects in (b) and (c) makes it possible for the construction to be made directly in the elevation.

In each of these three cases, a point P is chosen on the edge of the shape casting the shadow, which is represented by the point P′ in the elevation where the vertical angle of the sun is taken into account. The comparable point on the shadow is P″. The visualization of (c) is helped if you consider the appearance of the moon at the end of its first or third quarter.

## 4.7 EXERCISES

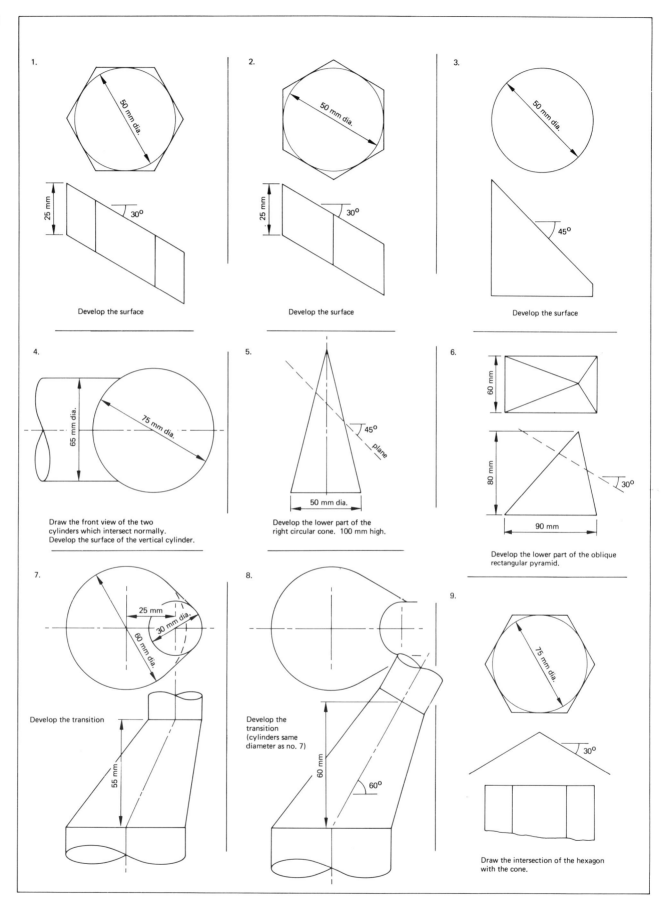

1. Develop the surface

2. Develop the surface

3. Develop the surface

4. Draw the front view of the two cylinders which intersect normally. Develop the surface of the vertical cylinder.

5. Develop the lower part of the right circular cone. 100 mm high.

6. Develop the lower part of the oblique rectangular pyramid.

7. Develop the transition

8. Develop the transition (cylinders same diameter as no. 7)

9. Draw the intersection of the hexagon with the cone.

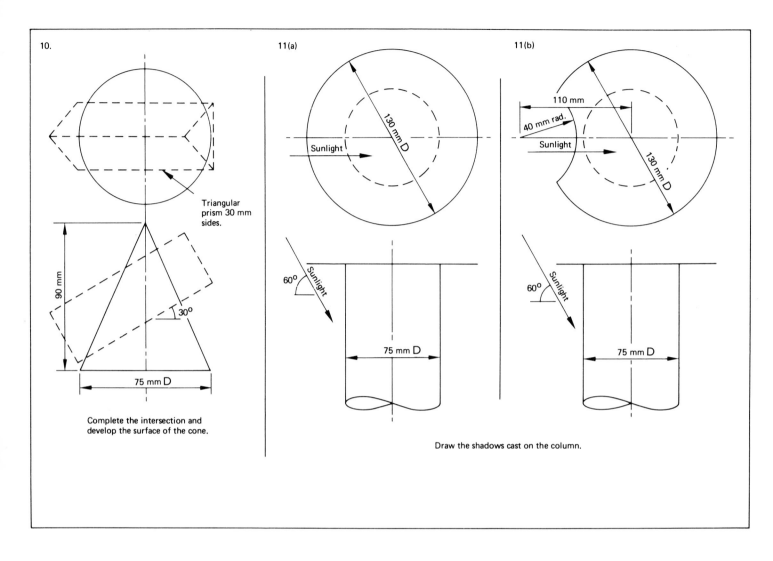

10.

Triangular
prism 30 mm
sides.

90 mm

30°

75 mm D

Complete the intersection and
develop the surface of the cone.

11(a)

130 mm D

Sunlight

60°
Sunlight

75 mm D

11(b)

110 mm

40 mm rad.

Sunlight

130 mm D

60°
Sunlight

75 mm D

Draw the shadows cast on the column.

# Chapter 5            **Conics**

*Road transport, Scotswood Bridge and approaches. A neat road bridge, of welded steel tied-arch construction with its deck suspended from the arch, together with the complicated approaches necessary to maintain traffic flow at peak hours. (Photograph supplied by Mitchell Construction, Kinnear Moodie Group)*

## 5.1 INTRODUCTION

A conic is a curve resulting from the inter-section of a plane with a cone. The civil engineer makes considerable use of these curves, either because they are pleasing shapes that are also structurally functional, or because they appear in his calculations.

The graphical derivation of the conic is a useful exercise, for the engineering student, in three-dimensional thinking and auxiliary views. The derived curves have useful applications in practice.

## 5.2 DERIVATION

The four fundamental conics, the circle, the ellipse, the parabola, and the hyperbola, may be obtained as the sections of a right circular cone, as shown in Fig. 5.1.

The axis of a right circular cone passes through the centre of the circular base and is normal to it.

(a) The circle is a section on a plane nor-mal to the axis of the cone.

(b) The ellipse is a section on a plane, other than the one described in (a), that cuts right through the cone.

(c) The hyperbola is a section on a plane which makes a larger angle with the base than the side of the cone makes. Note that this plane can cut another cone balanced symmetrically on top of the first cone.

(d) The parabola is a section on a plane parallel to the sloping edge.

5.1    *The four sections of a cone.*

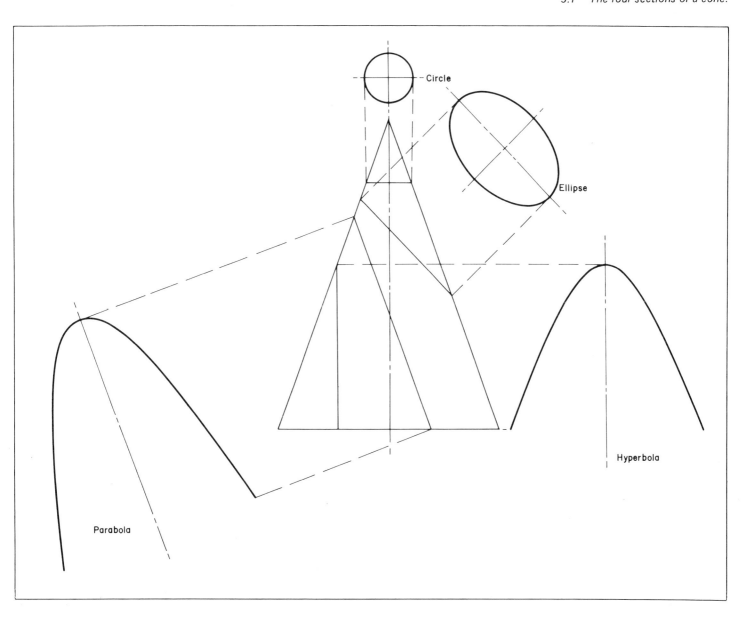

## 5.3 CONSTRUCTION OF A CONIC FROM A GIVEN CONE

Figure 5.2 shows a plane, an, cutting through a right circular cone to produce a parabola.

The method described can also be used for an ellipse or hyperbola. It consists in taking horizontal sections of the cone.

(a) Set off equal increments along the plane, an, in the elevation, ab, bc, etc.
Note: an will have a finite length for the ellipse and should be divided into equal increments so that the construction is symmetrical. It is difficult to draw a symmetrical shape through points arranged asymmetrically.

(b) Take sections of the cone at a, b, c, etc., which will appear in the plan as circles.

(c) The intersecting plane will cut the circles in the plan at a', b'b', c'c', etc.,

vertically above the points a, b, and c in the elevation. The lines b'b', c'c', etc., will be the true widths of the parabola at a, b, c, etc., and can be plotted on the side elevation where a fore-shortened view of the parabola will appear. An auxiliary view will be necessary to show the true shape of the parabola.

## 5.4 FOUR METHODS OF GRAPHICAL CONSTRUCTION OF AN ELLIPSE

The ellipse was probably used more extensively in the nineteenth century when masonry and brick arch bridges were being constructed. The ellipse replaced the circular arches as it allowed long spans to be made without excessive rise. The arch Brunnel put over the River Thames at Maidenhead was so flat, it is said that he was made to leave the timber formwork in place in case the arch fell down.

5.2   *The general geometric construction of a conic section applied to the parabola.*

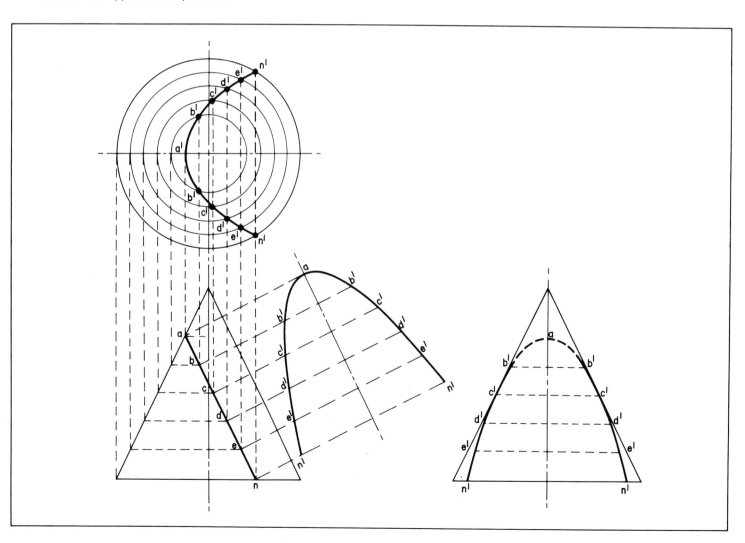

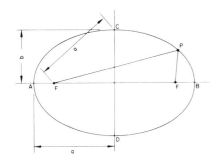

5.3   Graphical construction of an ellipse by
      string and pegs.

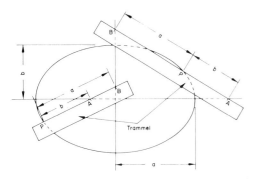

5.4   Graphical construction of an ellipse by
      the trammel method.

He is reputed to have eased the timber before he left the bridge. In any case, the bridge still stands and carries rail loads unthought of when it was built.

### (a) Strings and pegs

Figure 5.3 shows how an ellipse may be generated by a point moving so that the sum of its distance from two points, the foci, is constant and equal to the major axis. This method is little used on the drawing board, but is used out of doors, often by groundsmen.

The foci are located by swinging arcs, with a radius a equal to half the major axis, from the ends of the minor axis C or D, to cut the major axis at the points F.

Set up pegs at the foci. Make a loop with a piece of cord of length (AB + FF), i.e., the major axis plus the separation of the foci. Keep the cord tight round the pegs; the point P will then trace out the required ellipse.

### (b) Trammel method

This is a useful method in practice as points can be located at will to define the tighter parts of the curve.

The trammel, see Fig. 5.4, can be of folded paper or card. Set off the semimajor axis a and the semiminor axis b in either of the two ways shown, and mark the points A, B, and P.

Move the trammel so that B moves up and down the minor axis while A moves along the major axis. The point P traces out the ellipse.

### (c) Concentric circle method

Draw a pair of concentric circles with radii equal to half the two axes of the ellipse, see Fig. 5.5.

From the centre of the circles, draw radial lines to cut the circles at A and B. A point P on the ellipse is located at the intersection of a vertical from A and a horizontal from B.

Locate a small number of points P to start with and provide extra ones where needed to define the tighter parts of the curve.

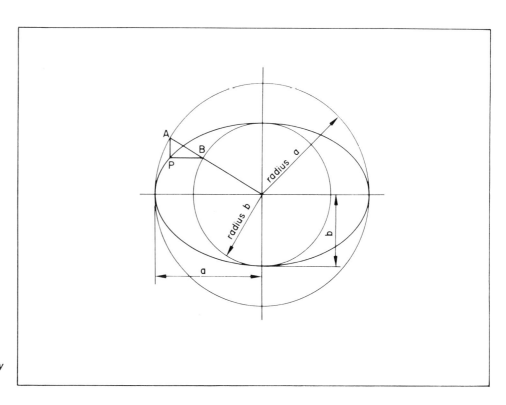

5.5   Graphical construction of an ellipse by
      concentric circles.

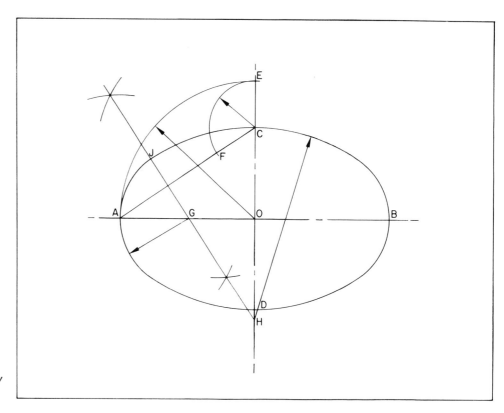

5.6  *Graphical construction of an ellipse by*
     *approximate arcs.*

**(d)  Approximate arcs method**

It is often convenient to draw an approximate
ellipse for illustrative purposes and the following method is quick and effective (Fig. 5.6).

(a)  Set up the two axes.

(b)  Join AC.

(c)  Centre O, swing an arc, radius OA, to cut
     OC produced at E.

(d)  Centre C, swing an arc, radius CE, to cut
     CA at F.

(e)  Locate points G and H where the per-
     pendicular bisector of AF cuts OA and
     OD, produced if necessary.

(f)  Centre H, swing an arc, radius HC, to
     complete the part of the ellipse CJ.

(g)  Centre G, swing an arc, radius GA, to J.

It is useful, when sketching, to draw an
ellipse as two pairs of circular arcs; the result
is very realistic, and more symmetrical than
would otherwise be achieved.

**5.5  TWO METHODS OF GRAPHICAL
       CONSTRUCTION OF A PARABOLA**

The parabola is perhaps the curve most used
in civil engineering. You will be well advised

to remember at least one quick graphical
method of construction, probably method (a)
described below.

A French curve, with a good range of parabolae, is essential for good results. Many
French curves are too small and their curves
too sharp for constructing most parabolae.

In practice, you may find that the greatest
use of parabolae will be in constructing bending moment diagrams for distributed loads.
Time can be saved as shown in Fig. 5.8, if the
points of maxima and minima moment are
found and the parabolae between them constructed graphically rather than by calculating
the moments at a number of points, plotting
them, and then drawing the curve.

Find the value of the bending moment at as
many points as possible, in this example A,
B, C, and D. The maximum positive moment
will occur where the shear force is a minimum.
The parabolae AB' and BC' may then be constructed.

Note that the area of a parabola is 2/3 the
area of the enveloping rectangle.

The parabola is sometimes considered to be

more pleasing aesthetically than the circular
arc. Even when the parabola is very flat, for
example, at the springings of a flat arch, the
subtle difference is more satisfying to the eye
than a continuous arc. From a practical aspect, the slope at the outer ends of a parabola
is flatter than at the same points of a circular
arch with the same span and rise. This often
makes the parabola more convenient for
bridge deck profiles. Few things are more
pleasing visually than the sweep of the cables
of a suspension bridge and these are very
nearly parabolic.

**(a)  Graphical construction to a given rise and
       span**

To draw a parabola of span b and height d,
as shown in Fig. 5.7 (a), the following
instructions should be remembered. This
is the most likely way a parabola will be
specified.

(a)  Divide OA into any number of equal
     parts and number them as shown. Drop
     vertical lines from the points 1, 2, 3,
     etc.

(b)  Divide AB into the same number of

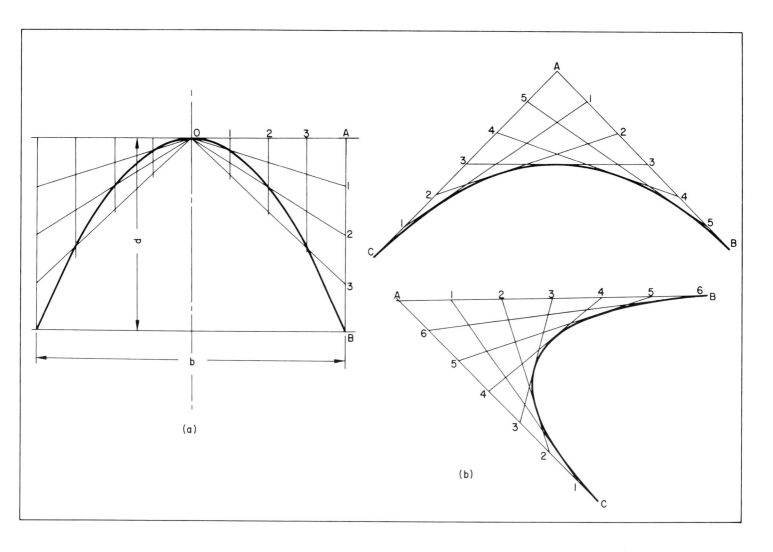

(a)

(b)

5.7   Graphical construction of a parabola.
      (a) To a given rise and span.
      (b) Between two given tangents.

equal parts and number them as shown.

(c) Points P on the parabola will occur at the intersection of the sloping lines O1, O2, O3, etc., with the verticals through 1, 2, 3, etc.

**(b) Graphical construction between two given tangents**

A parabola, drawn between two given tangents, see Fig. 5.7 (b), is useful for sketching vertical road curves quickly so that alternative schemes can be appraised. Levels for construction of the chosen scheme would then be calculated. The method is also applicable to skewed parabolae which might be needed for aesthetic reasons.

(a) Produce the tangents to intersect at A. The parabola meets the tangent at B and C.

(b) Divide AC and AB into the same number of equal parts.

(c) Number one tangent from the tangent point C to the intersection point A, and the other one in the reverse direction, A to B.

(d) Join points with the same number, 1 and 1, 2 and 2, 3 and 3, etc., to form a series of additional tangents to the parabola.

(e) Draw the parabola as a smooth curve within the envelope of tangents.

*5.8*  *Uniformly distributed loading on a beam giving rise to a parabolic bending moment diagram.*

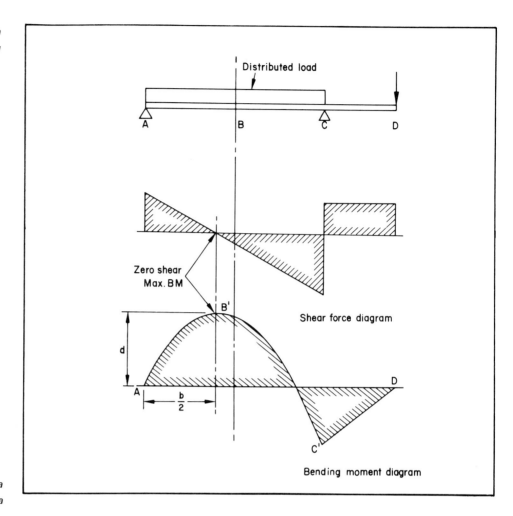

*5.9*  *Graphical construction of an hyperbola given the assymptotes AO, AB and a single point P.*

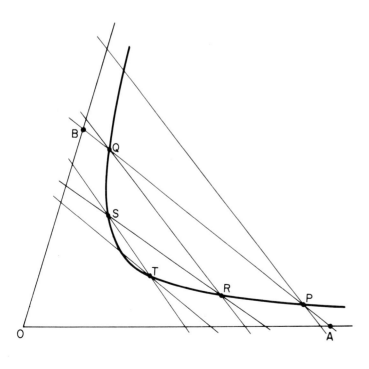

## 5.6 GRAPHICAL CONSTRUCTION OF AN HYPERBOLA

Figure 5.9 shows how to draw an hyperbola given the asymptotes OA, OB and a single point P.

The construction is based on the fact that intercepts AP, BQ, on a chord of the hyperbola, are equal.

(a) Draw any chord across the axes or asymptotes to pass through point P.

(b) Measure intercept AP and set off BQ equal to AP.

(c) Draw any further chords through P or Q and establish additional points R, S, T, etc., as necessary.

## 5.7 EXERCISES

1. The ellipse

   Compare the three methods of drawing an ellipse, trammel, concentric circles, and approximate arcs, by constructing an ellipse, 150 x 100 mm, by each method on tracing paper and laying the ellipses over each other. Then construct ellipses with various sizes of major axis to see where the differences are more marked.

2. The parabola

   (a) Draw two parabolae by the method given in section 5.5 (a):

      (i) 60 mm rise by 180 mm span.

      (ii) 150 mm rise by 75 mm span.

   (b) Draw the bending moment diagram for a beam 30 m long, supported at one end and at 6 m from the other end, with a total load of 100 Kg/m over its whole length.

3. The hyperbola

   (a) Complete a rectangular hyperbola between the x and y axes if it passes through the point (4.1).

   (b) Draw an hyperbola between asymptotes 60° apart which passes through a bisector of the angle 30 mm from the intersection.

4. Draw an elevation of an arch 20 m rise by 60 m span and compare the three curves:

   (a) Circular arc.

   (b) Ellipse.

   (c) Parabola.

# Chapter 6          **Measured perspective**

*High Rise, a development at Tolworth, Surrey, consisting of a shopping centre, offices, and parking area. (Photograph supplied by the Cement and Concrete Association)*

## 6.1 INTRODUCTION

Although small objects can be shown satisfactorily in isometric projection, the lack of perspective makes it unsuitable for larger objects such as buildings, dams, etc. The human eye is used to seeing parallel lines converge as they run to infinity and is disturbed if they do not.

## 6.2 SINGLE POINT PERSPECTIVE

The simplest perspective drawing is single point perspective in which all parallels converge at one point. Single point perspective results if the centre of vision (see definitions below) is parallel with one axis of the scene, e.g., looking down a straight railway track or standing in a room facing one wall squarely and looking parallel to another.

Single point perspective is shown in Fig. 6.1 to which the following definitions apply.

(a) Station point (SP): The point from which the object or scene is viewed. It is better not to call it the view point in case the abbreviation VP is confused with the vanishing point, see (d) below.

(b) Horizon: The horizontal plane which contains the station point.

(c) Picture plane (PP): The plane on to which the perspective is projected.

(d) Vanishing point (VP): The point at which parallel lines seem to join to-

6.1 *Single point perspective: general construction showing how the size of the picture is controlled by the location of the picture plane.*

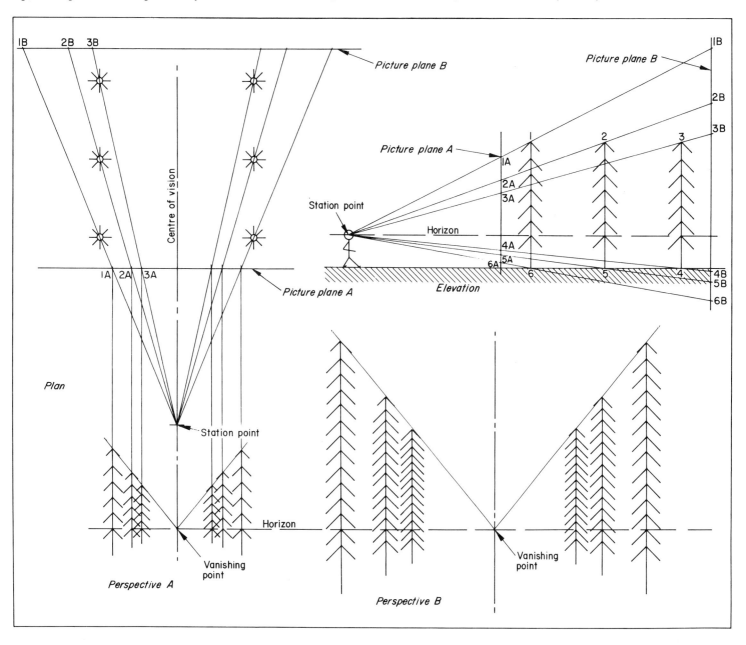

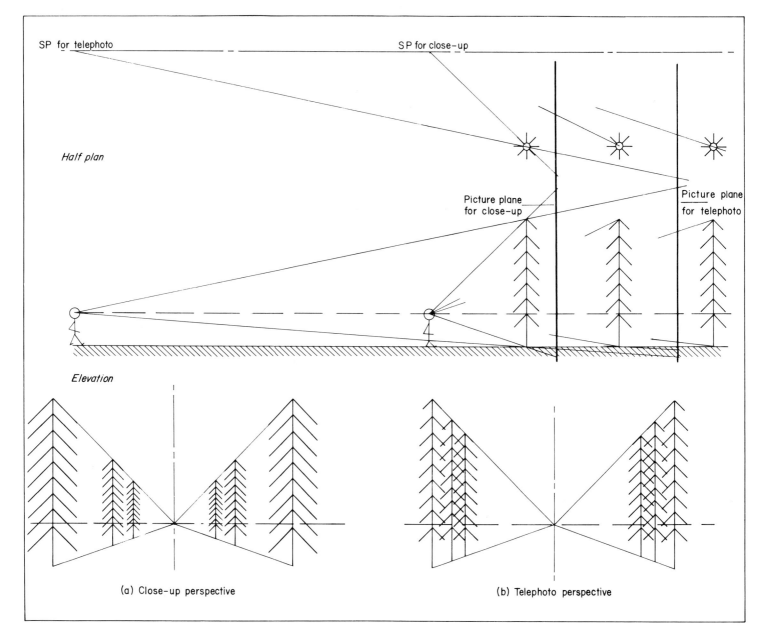

SP for telephoto

SP for close-up

Half plan

Picture plane
for close-up

Picture plane
for telephoto

Elevation

(a) Close-up perspective

(b) Telephoto perspective

6.2  *Single point perspective showing how
the type of perspective is controlled by
the location of the station point.*

gether or vanish. Left-hand and right-hand points are indicated by VPL and VPR.

(e) Centre of vision (CV): The optical axis of the construction.

The distance of the station point from the nearest point of the object or scene will have a considerable effect on the perspective. A close station point exaggerates the perspective by making the nearest tree seem much larger than the succeeding ones, see Fig. 6.2 (a). This technique is often used by advertising illustrators when they want to exaggerate some feature, for example, the interior of a small car can be made to appear cavernous. If the station point is too far away, the col-

lapsed perspective of the telephoto lens is obtained. Objects seem to be very closely packed with little loss of height from front to back of the scene, see Fig. 6.2 (b). A normal perspective effect is gained if the angle between the lines joining the eye to the extreme points of the object does not exceed 30°, either vertically or horizontally.

Natural perspectives are obtained with the horizon at eye level when standing, about 1.5 m above the ground. A lower horizon often gives a dramatic effect which architects like, while a bird's-eye view can clarify the layout of a project.

The plane on which the picture is to be projected should be located where it will give

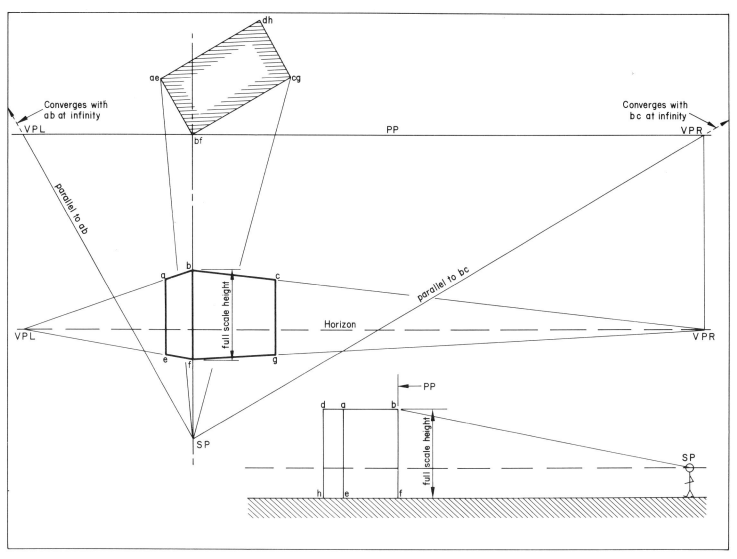

a finished picture of the required size. Picture plane B in Fig. 6.1 gives a larger picture than picture plane A without affecting the perspective. For picture plane A, imagine that a piece of glass has been placed between the observer and the scene so that a tracing can be made. Picture plane B can be considered as a screen on to which shadows of the objects are cast by a point source of light at the observer's eye. Note that the picture planes in Fig. 6.2 were located to make the nearest tree in each perspective the same height.

The centre of vision should be directed at the centre of interest. If there is no obvious centre of interest, it is usually better to split the view asymmetrically with the centre of vision, unless the symmetrical effect of Fig. 6.1 is required.

## 6.3 CONSTRUCTION OF SINGLE POINT PERSPECTIVE

This is shown in Fig. 6.1 and Fig. 6.2.
(a) Draw a plan and elevation to suitable scale.
(b) Decide upon and locate the horizon, station point, and picture plane.
(c) Draw lines from the station point to definitive points in the view (the tops and bottoms of the fir trees in Fig. 6.1) to cut the chosen picture plane.

The intercepts on the picture plane now represent the dimensions of the definitive points or lines. Heights appear in the elevation and widths in the plan.

It is often convenient to construct the perspective view directly below the plan, as for perspective A in Fig. 6.1, to save transferring dimensions. View B however was constructed by transferring all the dimensions.

The mechanics of single point perspective now appear; all parallels converge to a single vanishing point.

6.3 *Two point perspective: general construction showing how the vanishing points are located in the picture plane.*

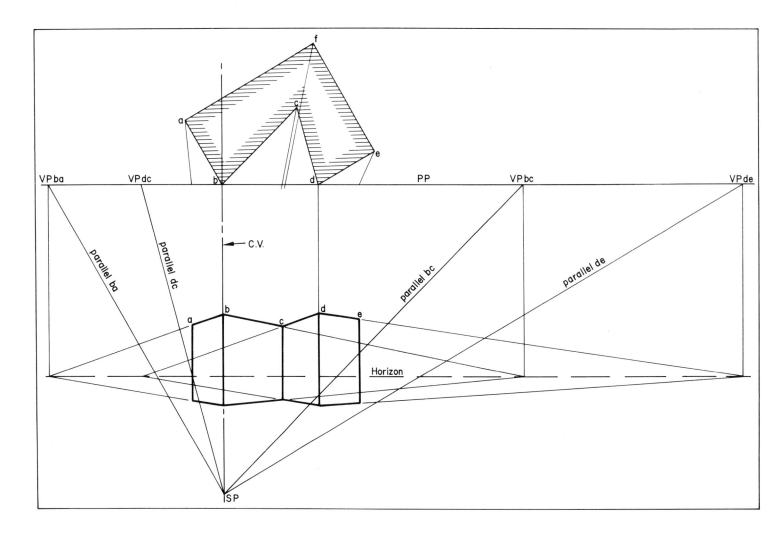

6.4   *Multi-point perspective which results it*
      *the faces of the object lie on several*
      *planes.*

**6.4 TWO POINT PERSPECTIVE**

If the centre of vision is not parallel with one
of the axes of the object, parallels in the perspective will converge on two or more vanishing points, see Fig. 6.3 and Fig. 6.4 respectively.

Two points of note arise in Fig. 6.3.

(a) The vanishing points are on the horizon
at infinity. Thus the line of sight from
the station point to the vanishing point
for the side of the block abfe will be
parallel to that side.

(b) For simple perspective exercises, an
elevation is usually not required if the
picture plane passes through the object. In Fig. 6.3, the corner of the block
bf lies in the picture plane and will
appear in the perspective at its full
height (according to the scale of the
plan).

There are four vanishing points in Fig. 6.4
because the four visible faces of the block
lie on different axes.

**6.5 CONSTRUCTION OF TWO POINT
PERSPECTIVE**

Refer to Fig. 6.5.

(a) Draw a plan view. A good impression
is obtained if the axes of the block are
at 30° and 60° to the picture plane.

(b) Make the nearest corner the centre of
interest and draw the centre of vision
through it.

(c) Locate the station point so that the
maximum included angle is 30°.

(d) Draw the picture plane to give the
perspective view of the required size
and then locate the vanishing points by
drawing lines through the station point
parallel to the axes of the block to cut
the picture plane.

*Note:* At this stage, it often happens
that the vanishing points are off
the paper. So, for routine exercises, it is sensible to work
backwards by locating the picture plane first, putting the

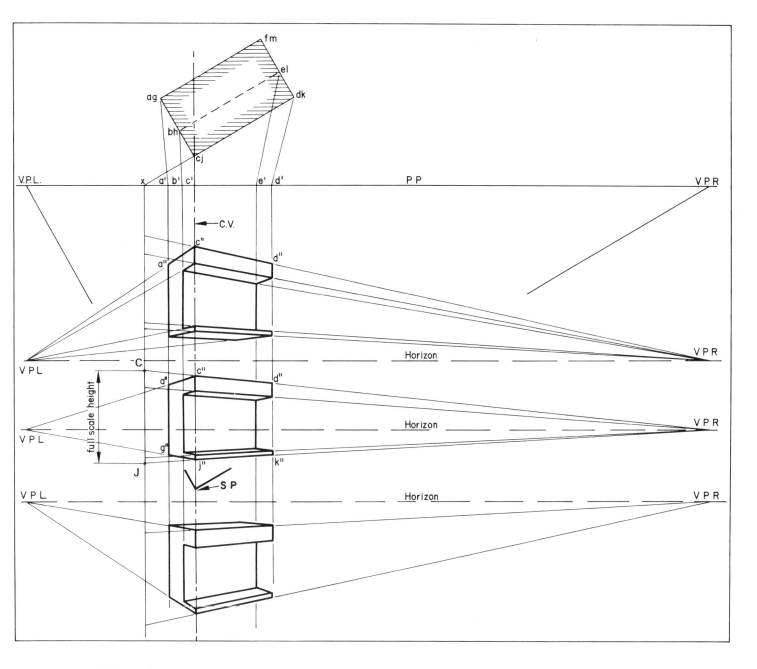

vanishing points at each end of it, and then locating the station point by dropping lines from the vanishing points parallel to the axes of the object. Finally, erect the centre of vision from the station point and draw the plan of the block.

(e) Draw lines from definitive points on the object abcde towards the station point to cut the picture plane at a' b' c' d' e'. It is better not to continue the lines to the station point as the mass of radiating lines can obscure subsequent construction.

(f) Start the perspective view by drawing its horizon and erect the first vertical.

*Note:* In the case of Fig. 6.3 the full scale height of the first vertical was used. In this case, the picture plane does not cut the object, therefore,

(i) project dc to meet the picture plane at X where cj will appear to its full scale height;

(ii) drop a vertical from X into the perspective view and set up CJ to its full scale height;

(iii) join C and J to the vanishing point right when the required

6.5 *Two point perspective: detailed construction showing the effect of raising or lowering the horizon beyond the vertical limits of the object.*

height c″ j″ will be the intercept on the vertical from c′, which, in this case, is also the centre of vision.

(g) Find d″ vertically below d′ and on the line from c″ to the vanishing point right.

Bird's-eye or worm's-eye impressions can be drawn by moving the horizon beyond the lower or upper limits of the object.

A distorted effect will be obtained if the horizon is removed too far from the vertical limits of the object because the verticals should then converge to vanishing points, see the three point perspective in Fig. 6.6 which is not pursued here.

Two point perspective can be adopted, as shown in Fig. 6.7, to give vertical perspective if the construction is based on an elevation instead of a plan. The centre of vision can be moved, like the horizon in the previous examples, to reveal the side of the object.

## 6.6 REALISTIC COMPLETION OF PERSPECTIVES

Any draughtsman can perform the mechanics of perspective drawing and end up with a characterless skeleton, only the gifted can bring perspectives to life, as shown in Fig. 6.8 (b). An engineer with a knowledge of perspective will at least be able to argue intelligently with the artist or architect who is to make the artist's impression of his project. The engineer might prevent too outrageous an interpretation being made, or provide the artist with an accurate skeleton to clothe.

In any case, an engineer should keep a sketch book of his ideas or ideas he has borrowed from other projects. A knowledge of perspective will speed and improve his sketches.

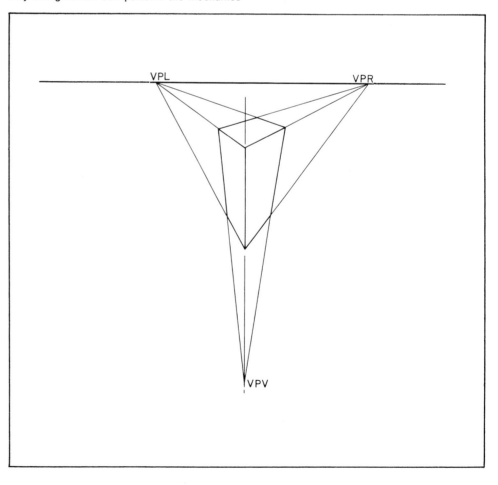

6.6    Three point perspective: general construction.

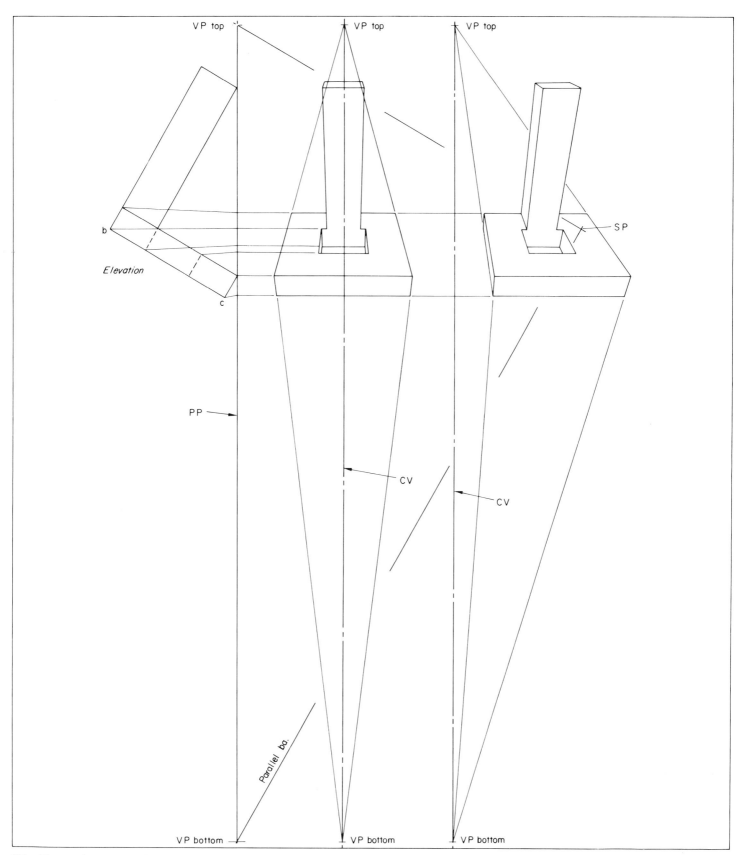

6.7 *Two point perspective adapted to give vertical perspective to a tall object. The construction is based upon an elevation instead of a plan.*

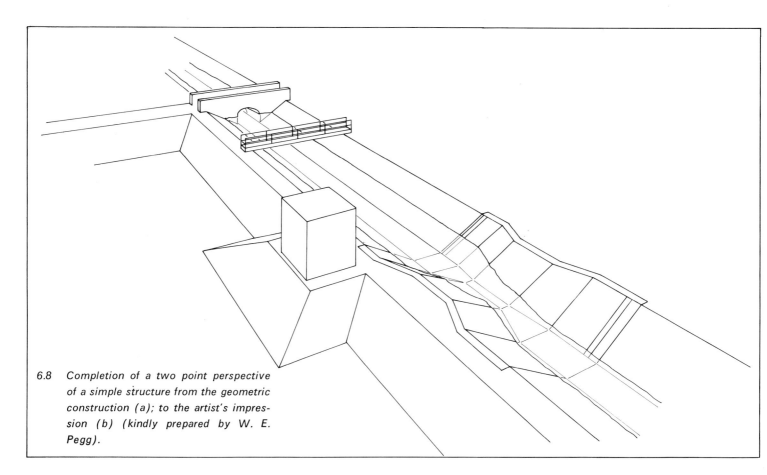

6.8    Completion of a two point perspective
of a simple structure from the geometric
construction (a); to the artist's impression (b) (kindly prepared by W. E.
Pegg).

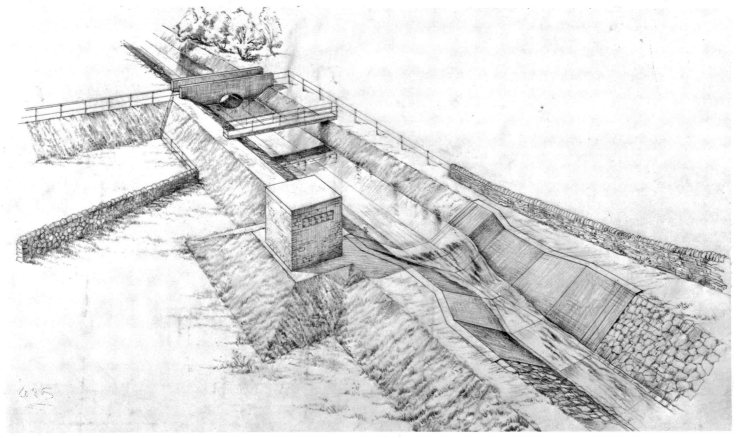

## 6.7 EXERCISES

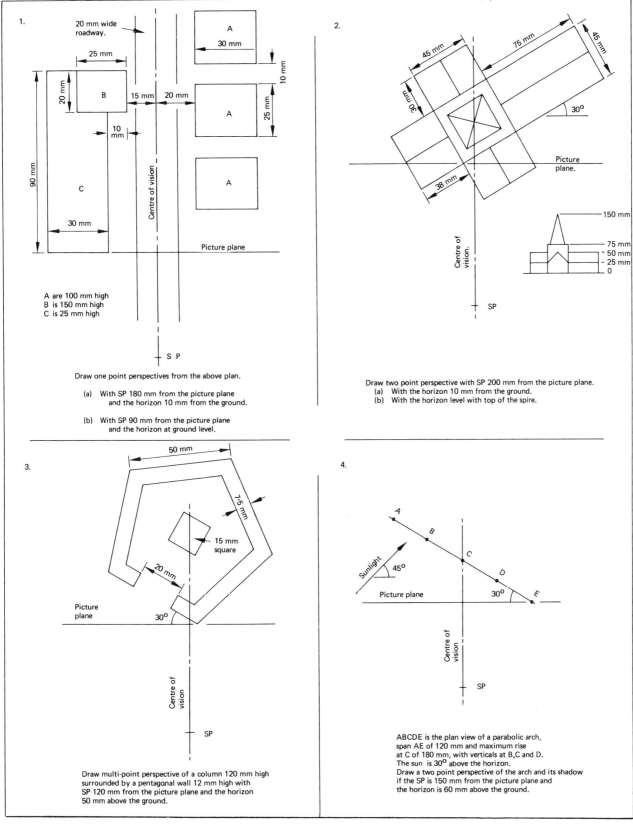

1.

20 mm wide roadway.

25 mm

20 mm

B

15 mm    20 mm

10 mm

90 mm

C

30 mm

Centre of vision

Picture plane

A

30 mm

10 mm

A

25 mm

A

A are 100 mm high
B is 150 mm high
C is 25 mm high

S P

Draw one point perspectives from the above plan.

(a) With SP 180 mm from the picture plane
and the horizon 10 mm from the ground.

(b) With SP 90 mm from the picture plane
and the horizon at ground level.

2.

45 mm    75 mm    45 mm

30 mm

30°

Picture plane.

38 mm

Centre of vision.

SP

150 mm

75 mm
50 mm
25 mm
0

Draw two point perspective with SP 200 mm from the picture plane.
(a) With the horizon 10 mm from the ground.
(b) With the horizon level with top of the spire.

3.

50 mm

7·5 mm

15 mm square

20 mm

Picture plane

30°

Centre of vision

SP

Draw multi-point perspective of a column 120 mm high
surrounded by a pentagonal wall 12 mm high with
SP 120 mm from the picture plane and the horizon
50 mm above the ground.

4.

A

B

C

D

E

Sunlight

45°

Picture plane

30°

Centre of vision

SP

ABCDE is the plan view of a parabolic arch,
span AE of 120 mm and maximum rise
at C of 180 mm, with verticals at B,C and D.
The sun is 30° above the horizon.
Draw a two point perspective of the arch and its shadow
if the SP is 150 mm from the picture plane and
the horizon is 60 mm above the ground.

**Further reading**

1. Capelle:

*Professional Perspective Drawing for Archi-
tects and Engineers*, McGraw-Hill Book Company Inc.

2. Martin:

*Design Graphics*, Collier- Macmillan.

Part Three            **In practice**

Chapter 7             **Drawing in practice—a case history**

*The new Dartford Tunnel. (Photograph supplied
by the New Civil Engineer)*

## 7.1 INTRODUCTION

In this chapter the development of civil engineering schemes will be studied very generally from conception to completion, indicating at each stage the type of drawings that can be involved. Many actual examples have been included.

For the purposes of the case history, it is assumed that a local authority is preparing a scheme large enough to require a special Act of Parliament for its execution. Consulting engineers might be engaged for the design and supervision of the construction, but this would not affect the type and range of drawings used.

The graphical programme is divided into simple steps relating to the general headings to each section.

## 7.2 FUTURE NEEDS

In addition to supervising the day to day running of his office and dealing with schemes already under construction, the engineer to any authority must be aware of future needs and make plans to meet them.

The city engineer, *inter alia*, must try to foresee future traffic congestion, the need to clear rundown residential areas, whether the sewage system and treatment works will be adequate in the future. The water engineer must be sure that, in addition to having enough water, see Fig. 7.1 (a) and (b), his treatment works are satisfactory and that his pipelines are biologically and structurally safe. The land drainage engineer must be sure that his watercourses, sluices, and locks are adequate and safe and that his pumping stations are large enough and up to date. The engineer responsible must know whether the airport runways and terminal buildings are large enough to meet future needs; whether the anchorage is deep enough for larger tankers; whether the track of the main line is still safe since the development of the nearby boggy land.

A guide to the solution of some of these problems lies in the trend of population in the area and the standard of living that will be expected within the time being considered.

If the area is a thriving one, as the south-eastern corner of England is at present, not only will the population increase, but the standard of living will tend to rise with associated increases in the *per capita* consumption of water and electricity. People will want more motor vehicles and aircraft, while they and their factories will create more sewage and waste, the latter often of increasing toxicity and with its associated problems.

Whether he is looked upon as prescient, courageous, optimistic, or a fool to try, the engineer must attempt to forecast his employers' requirements.

The need for thrift in expenditure or the spreading of funds as far as possible means that, at best, a scheme must not be completed too far in advance of needs, while the norm is often one crisis of survival after another.

Some authorities never catch up, but others are prepared to invest for the future. It is up to the engineer to try to understand his authority so that he can present to them the scheme they want or, better still, make them want the scheme he presents. In any case, well prepared, easily understood drawings will often carry the day for the engineer. A committee, not made conscious of their possible inability to read tricky engineering drawings, can be more receptive and amenable to new ideas.

## 7.3 SEARCHING FOR A SITE

Whether the engineer is looking for a site for a sewage works, railway siding, or reservoir, he will employ maps or aerial photographs to speed the search. Although Great Britain is covered by the most comprehensive system of mapping of any country in the world, the very best map cannot be interpreted fully without a visit, however cursory, to the site.

In addition to the wide range of topographical maps, the engineer has at his disposal maps of many diverse types, including geological, land use, population concentration, rainfall, etc.

While aerial photographs, vertical or oblique and preferably stereoscopic, are not generally available, every effort should be made to obtain them. One of the firms that specializes in this work may already have covered the area for some other purpose. No scheme of any size should be planned without aerial photographs. So many engineers sadly relate how a fault or hazard, that upset their plans and wasted time and money, was obvious when they subsequently examined aerial photographs. Complete interpretation of aerial photographs is a job for the specialist.

Some schemes, particularly in underdeveloped countries, often rely entirely on photographs and photogrammetry of the type shown in Fig. 8.17 (a) for site information. Where no reliable or up to date maps exist, aerial photographs backed up by ground control and speeded up by electronic measuring devices, are the only way of obtaining site information in a reasonable time and at reasonable cost. In our own relatively overdeveloped land, some local authorities use aerial photographs to find developments which have not been approved.

We are not concerned here with the social and political factors which influence the engineer when he is looking for a site, but they can be an even greater hazard than nature itself. The ponderous machinery of land acquisition, whether achieved voluntarily or compulsorily, and the time involved thereby can often influence the choice of site and result in a less suitable one being selected. Over half the time taken in completing a motorway can be consumed in the litigation and archaic processes of land acquisition. The engineer is not a tyrant needlessly dispossessing people of their houses and land. However, he must be prepared for many frustrations and delays to his plans while land agents and lawyers carry on their protracted negotiations.

The plans used to acquire land are important documents in this phase of the scheme. They are usually based on suitable *Ordnance Survey* sheets, often 1:2500 scale, with the land to be acquired indicated in some way, see Fig. 7.2. Usually, the land to be acquired is coloured red. Different colours are generally used for land required for working space and construction access or for land over which access may occasionally be required in the future, a wayleave. The preparation of these plans can consume much drawing office time. However, transparent photocopies of the appropriate *Ordnance Survey* sheet for making dyeline prints, are being used more and more to speed this work.

## 7.4 DESK STUDIES

When several suitable sites for a project present themselves, their topographical suitability can often be compared, with sufficient accuracy, from desk studies based upon site information taken from maps and other available sources. The feasibility studies for the Morecambe Bay and Solway barrages were carried out in this way.

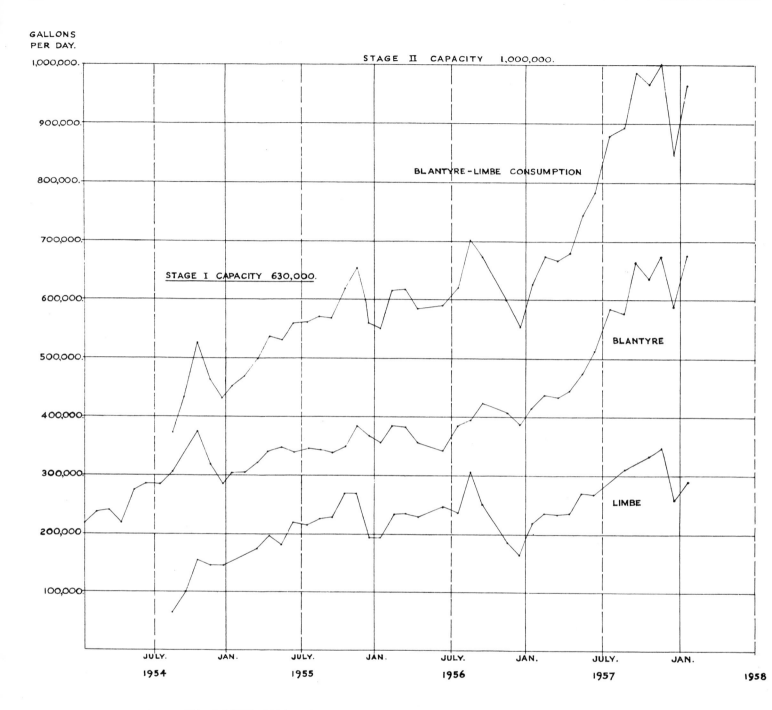

# BLANTYRE - LIMBE   WATER   CONSUMPTION

7.1   (a) *Record of water consumption for two African towns, showing the growth in consumption.*
*(Supplied by Scott & Wilson, Kirkpatrick & Partners)*

If, for example, a reservoir is to be sited in a given valley which has reasonably predictable geology, the preliminary calculations of reservoir depths and capacity can be based upon the contours shown on a map of suitable scale. The dam can be moved and further studies of depth/capacity relationships can be carried out, without moving from the desk and without stirring up local feeling and causing unnecessary alarm to residents before a scheme is known to be feasible.

A development of the desk study is one from a car window. With maps of the correct scale, vast areas can be covered in a few days. For example, the preliminary alignment of a water main nearly two hundred miles long was outlined in two or three days by this method and was surprisingly close to the finished design which emerged several months later. Some local survey work had to be carried out where relative levels over flat slopes could not be determined by eye.

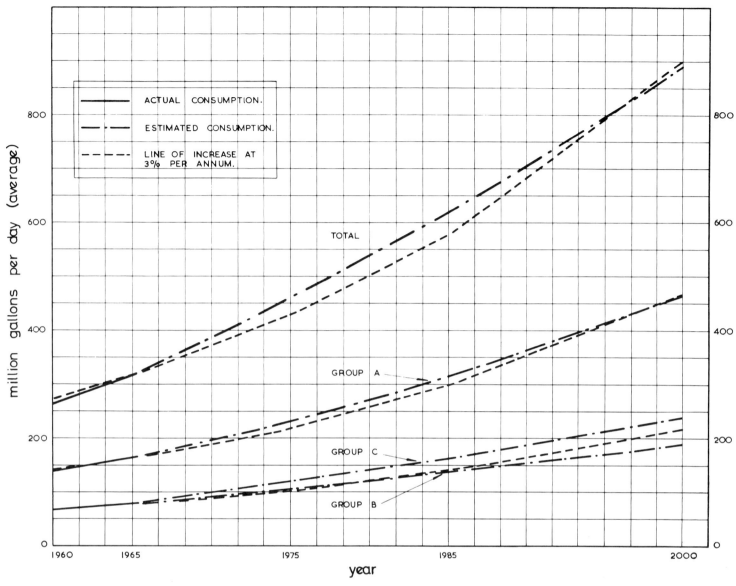

ACTUAL   CONSUMPTION.

ESTIMATED   CONSUMPTION.

LINE OF   INCREASE   AT
3% PER   ANNUM.

TOTAL

GROUP   A

GROUP   C

GROUP   B

million gallons per day (average)

year

Sometimes it may be necessary to amplify the information obtained from the map with limited site surveys and investigations of sub-soil and geological conditions.

Often the design process is easier in difficult terrain than in more amenable areas. A mountain road may have only one route which is physically possible, but a road across easy country can have many variants, economic, political, or social, all of which must be studied. Moreover, engineering in difficult terrain is more interesting.

Here is an extreme example of this type of study. The alignment, survey, and tender drawings for a seven mile stretch of mountain road were completed in three winter months by using the 1:2500 *Ordnance Survey* sheets as background. The route was first sketched on to the maps by eye, on site. The curves

and geometry were then adjusted to conform to vehicular speed requirements. Finally, cross sections were taken for the combined process of designing vertical curves and balancing the cut and fill of earthworks as far as possible. The intersection points of the straights, the basis for setting out the curves, were located on site by measurements from such topographical detail as existed, corners of stone walls, gateways, etc., see Fig. 7.3. Only then were the angles between straights measured by theodolite so that the curves and transitions could be ranged in. By delaying and reducing the quantity of time consuming detail, survey, and drawing, a tight contractural deadline was met, although much more responsibility was thrown upon the site supervisory staff. Originally, it was intended to use 1:500 photographic enlargements of the 1:2500

*(b) Trend curve of water supply for the basin of the River Trent recording demands to date and forecasting future needs in three subdistricts as well as in the basin as a whole. (Supplied by the Engineer to the Trent River Authority)*

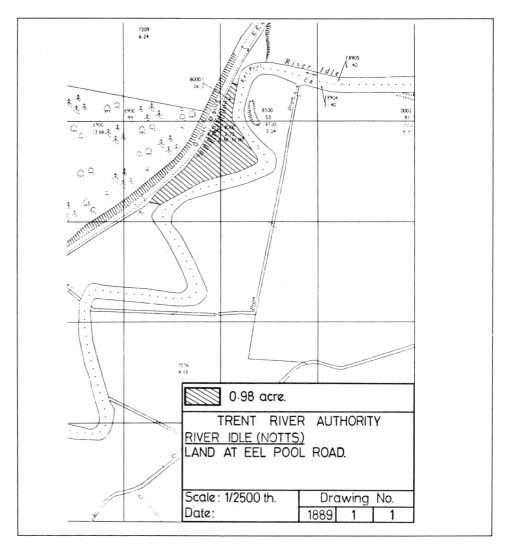

7.2   *Drawing showing the land to be pur-*
      *chased for a small scheme; a land plan.*
      *It is based on a photographic reproduc-*
      *tion of a 1:2500 Ordnance Survey map.*
      *(Supplied by the Engineer to the Trent*
      *River Authority)*

*Ordnance Survey* sheets as background for this job, but the increased thickness of line, with correspondingly fuzzier edges, offset any increased accuracy obtained from the use of larger drawings.

Desk studies must be carried out carefully and to the limits of the accuracy imposed by the data used. If two sites are of relatively equal merit, rough work in the preliminary stages can lead to a wrong decision which might only be discovered when much expensive site investigation had already been carried out.

## 7.5 SITE SURVEYS AND INVESTIGATION

After a desk study has shown that a site is suitable, it must be investigated more fully before engineering design can begin. Few sites are properly investigated. Sometimes there is insufficient time, but often the engineer cannot persuade his employers that

they should spend their money on anything apparently so unproductive.

Subsoil investigations are slow and expensive, usually consisting of a number of carefully referenced boreholes from which samples are taken and in which *in situ* tests are made. There must, however, be uncertainty about the subsoil in the gaps between boreholes. It is incredible how many small but nasty geological faults are missed by site investigation only to be revealed once excavation for the foundations begins.

Shallow sites can be investigated by trenches or pits which enable larger samples to be taken for testing and the substrata to be seen. These are more expensive than borings and can be a nuisance when work actually commences on the site.

More faith is being placed in the results of seismic and resistivity tests for quicker, nondestructive investigations. As they become

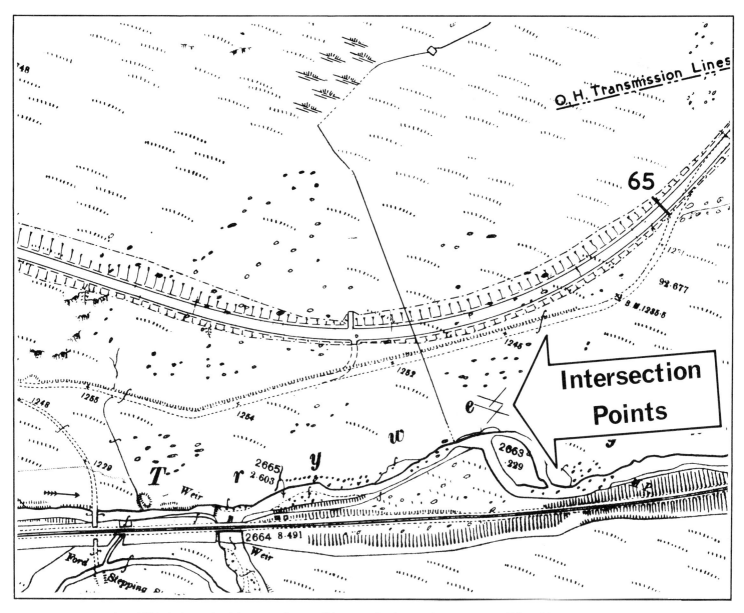

7.3   Alignment of a road in a mountainous area of Wales. The drawing is based on a 1:2500 Ordnance Survey map.
(Supplied by the County Surveyor to Merioneth County Council)

more common, greater skill is being gained in the interpretation of the results.

Most of the information gained from site investigations can be interpreted more quickly if it is presented graphically.

Typical borehole logs and reference plans, are shown in Figs. 7.4 and 7.5.

## 7.6 EVIDENCE TO OWN COMMITTEE

Few engineeers these days are employed by a completely autocratic individual from whom a quick decision can be obtained. More usually, the team which the engineer heads has to persuade another team (the committee), headed by a chairman, that a scheme is suitable. So many compromises are effected by both sides because of outside influences (planning and amenity considerations, land-scaping, politics, etc.) that, unless a very careful diary is kept of this gestation period, it is difficult afterwards to pin down responsibility for a particular decision, especially if there is any recrimination. The introductory passages of many technical papers describing projects illustrate this process of debate, which is all part of the design process. Sometimes it becomes obvious that the chronicler either cannot remember the intricate steps followed at this stage or cannot reconcile them with his own ideas.

Many engineers to public authorities become skilled salesmen of ideas and know how to present their schemes attractively to their employers. In addition to facts, figures, and balance sheets, the engineer uses many graphic forms of presentation: maps, eleva-

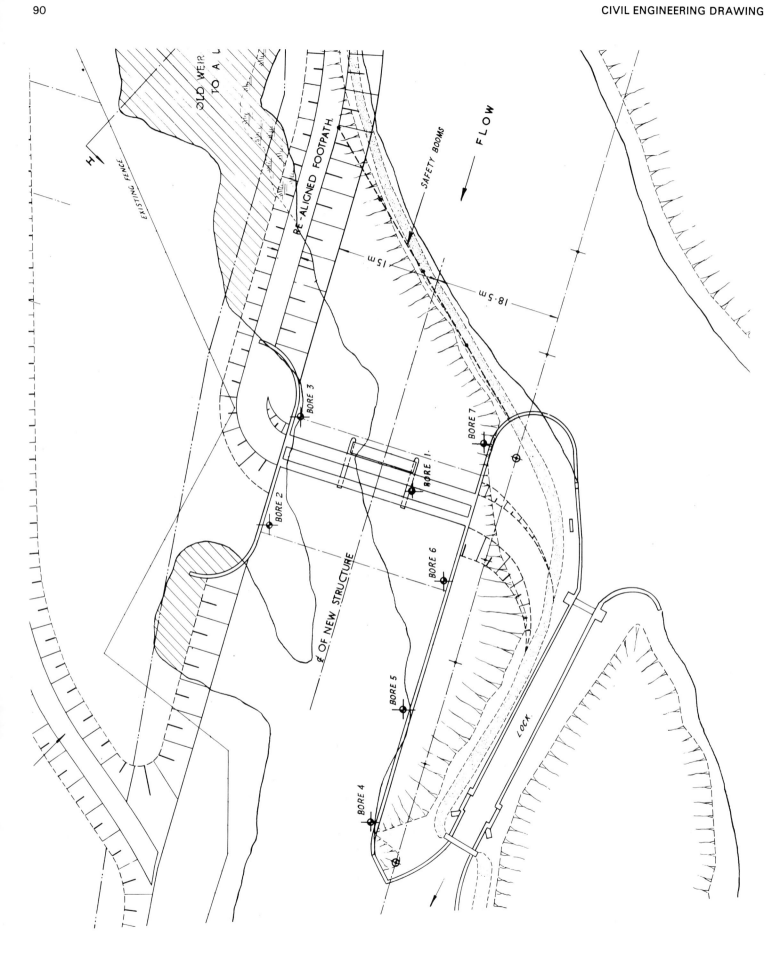

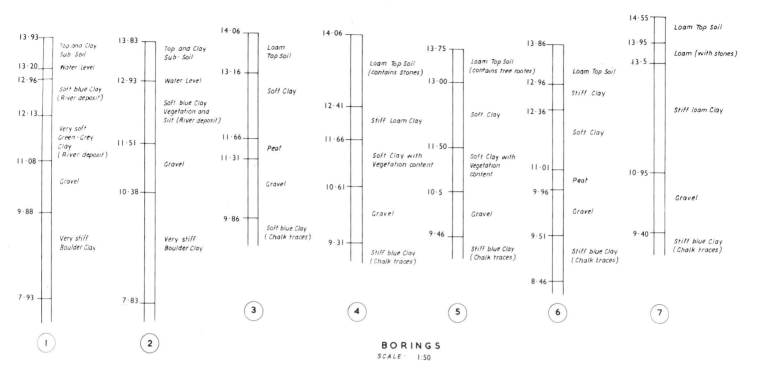

BORINGS
SCALE: 1:50

tions and sections, perspectives, and artist's impressions.

A committee's attention can be directed, by means of cartoons, to a point that the engineer wants resolved. Cartoons are drawings shorn of unnecessary detail and complication, see Fig. 7.6. They frequently accentuate a single aspect of a scheme. They should be simple, bold, and aided by the skilful use of colour.

All drawings to be used by a committee should be easy to handle. It is better to have special A4 drawings made, which can be bound into a report, rather than waste time and tempers while the members of the committee struggle to unfold and flatten larger drawings.

## 7.7 PARLIAMENTARY EVIDENCE

Our freedom of action is always limited, whether we are children depending on our parents' patience or a public body bounded by Parliamentary statute.

7.4 (a) Part of a working drawing showing the location of site investigation boreholes on the alignment of new sluice works. (Supplied by the Engineer to the Great Ouse River Authority. Eaton Socon Sluice Improvement)

If a civil engineering project extends to works or areas beyond the statutory limits of an authority, a special Act of Parliament or a Parliamentary Order must be sought.

An authority's submission to Parliament is called a Bill, which must be approved by the most democratic assembly possible, a town or city meeting for example, before being deposited at Westminster.

A very large number of special Acts of Parliament were sponsored by the newly formed railway companies about the middle of the nineteenth century. Each company had to prepare and give evidence before its own Parliamentary Committee with the engineer as the most important witness and coordinator. Communications then were primitive and most engineers connected with railways and similar large projects set up offices in Westminster to be close to Parliament. They could thus be called upon to organize and give evidence without wasting time at the expense of their normal professional affairs. The newly built thoroughfare, Victoria Street, offered modern accommodation for these pioneers. It is only now, a little over a century later, that many of the successors of these early engineers are moving to the provinces, partly on account of high office rents and difficult travelling conditions. Most of the original Victorian dwellings, too, are being demolished for more intensive development.

7.4 (b) Details of the boreholes shown in (a) taken from another part of the same drawing. (Supplied by the Engineer to the Great Ouse River Authority. Eaton Socon Sluice Improvement)

7.5 Two pages from a site investigation report.
   (a) Location of boreholes and site plan.
   (b) Log of one of the boreholes.
      (Supplied by Sarel of Watford, with permission of the Department of Highways and Transportation of the Greater London Council)

(see following two pages)

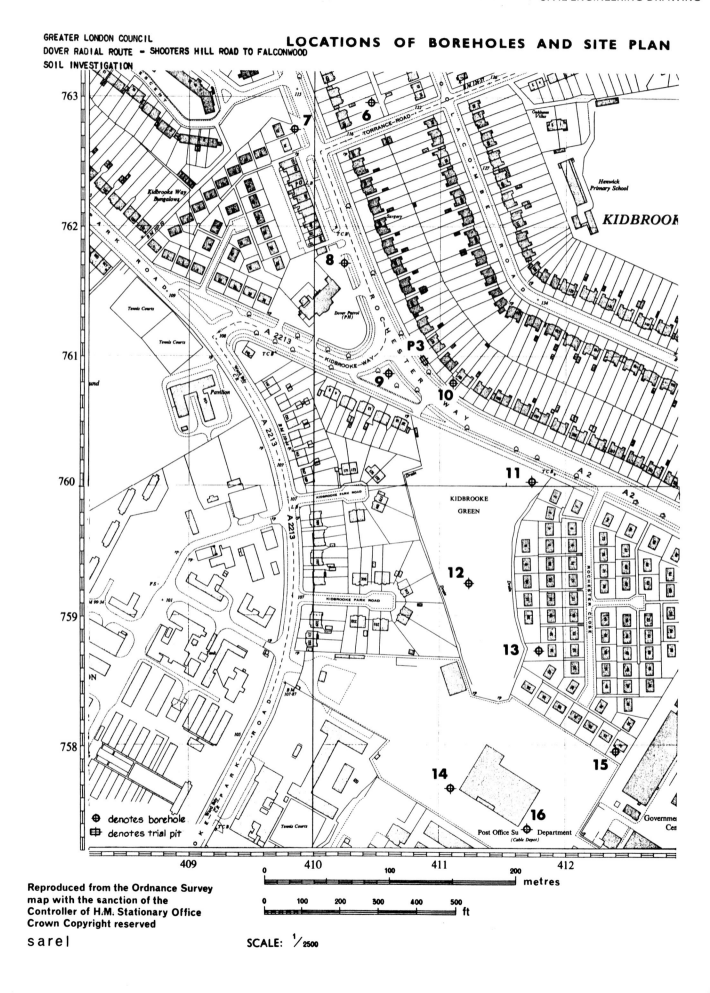

s a r e l                                    SCALE: $\frac{1}{2500}$

GREATER LONDON COUNCIL
DOVER RADIAL ROUTE - SHOOTERS HILL ROAD TO FALCONWOOD
SOIL INVESTIGATION

**RECORD OF BOREHOLE 9**

| | | |
|---|---|---|
| Type of Boring | shell and auger | |
| Dia of boring | 8in to 18.30m / 6in to 20.50m | |
| Lining tubes | 8in to 14.80m / 6in to 20.10m | |

Ground level 36.15m OD
Date started
Date completed

| Scale ft m | Date and Depth of Boring | Depth of Casing (m) | Water Level (m) | Samples Depth (m) | Samples Type | Change of Strata Legend | Depth (m) | Reduced Level | Description of Strata | |
|---|---|---|---|---|---|---|---|---|---|---|
| | 6-11-68 | nil | | 0.30 | D | | | | MADE GROUND - mainly topsoil, ashes, firm brown and grey silty clay, sand and occasional gravel | Sand/cement |
| 1 | 1.20 | nil 0.90 | seepage | 0.90 0.90-1.35 | D U4(26) | | 1.05 | 35.10 | Stiff brown and grey silty CLAY with pockets of brown sand and occasional fine gravel | |
| 2 | | 1.50 | | 1.70-2.15 | U4(20) | | 2.15 | 34.00 | | |
| 10 3 | 3.50 | 1.50 | nil | 2.45-2.90 | U4(27) | | | | Stiff brown and grey silty CLAY with partings and pockets of brown fine sand | |
| 4 | 7-11-68 | 1.50 | 2.60 | 3.50 3.95-4.40 | D&W U4(32) | | 3.95 | 32.20 | | |
| 5 | | 3.50 3.50 | | 4.90 | D | | | | Very stiff dark grey silty CLAY with partings of brown fine sand | |
| 20 6 | | 3.50 3.50 | | 5.50 5.65-6.10 | D U4(34) | | 5.50 | 30.65 | | |
| 7 | | 3.50 | | 7.15 | D | | | | Stiff fissured dark brown-grey silty CLAY | |
| 8 | ·8.40 | 3.50 3.50 | ▼ | 7.45-7.90 8.25 | U4(36) D | | 8.25 | 27.90 | | seal |
| 30 9 | 9.15 8-11-68 | 8.55 9.15 | 4.40 5.65 | 8.70-9.00 9.15 | C(48) & B W | | | | Very dense black rounded GRAVEL with some grey fine sand | sand ∎ seal |
| 10 | | 9.30 | | 9.45-9.75 | C(159) & B | | | | | |
| 11 | | 10.20 | | 10.35-10.65 | C(56) & B | | 10.80 | 25.35 | | |
| 40 12 | | 10.95 11.75 | | 11.15-11.35 11.90-12.20 | S(100) & B S(129) & B | | | | Very dense dark grey fine SAND with some shells | Excavated material |
| 13 | | 12.50 | | 12.65-12.75 | S(50) & B | | | | | |
| 14 | | 13.25 | | 13.40-13.55 | S(81) & B | | 13.85 | 22.30 | Very dense dark grey silty fine SAND with traces of shells | |
| 50 15 | 15.25 9-11-68 | 14.00 14.80 14.80 | 6.10 5.65 | 14.15-14.50 14.80 | S(85) & B D | | 14.65 | 21.50 | Cemented SHELLS | |
| 16 | | 14.80 14.80 | | 16.30 16.45-16.90 | D U4(78) | | 16.15 | 20.00 | | |
| 17 | | 14.80 | | 17.35 | D | | | | Stiff dark grey silty CLAY with shells | |
| 60 18 | | 14.80 | | 18.60 | D | | 18.30 18.45 | 17.85 17.70 | Cemented SHELLS | |
| 19 | | 14.80 | | 18.75-19.20 | U4(86) | | | | Very stiff dark grey silty CLAY with shells | |
| 20 | 20.10 11-11-68 20.50 | 14.80 20.10 20.10 20.10 | 5.80 5.35 5.35 | 19.65 20.25-20.50 | D U4(130)* | | | | | |
| 70 21 | | | | | | | | | END OF BOREHOLE Depth: 20.50m Elevation: 15.65m OD | |

**Key**
▼ denotes ground water first encountered
U4( ) „ 4 in dia undisturbed sample
U1½( ) „ 1½ in „ „ „
D „ disturbed sample
B „ bulk sample
W „ water sample
S( ) „ standard penetration test
C( ) „ cone penetration test
(24) „ number of blows
• „ sample not recovered
∎ „ piezometer tip

**Remarks**

A rock chisel was used between depths of 14.65m and 16.15m

Scale: 1 : 100  **FIG 23**

Form No. G12 (9/68)

soil and rock engineering limited

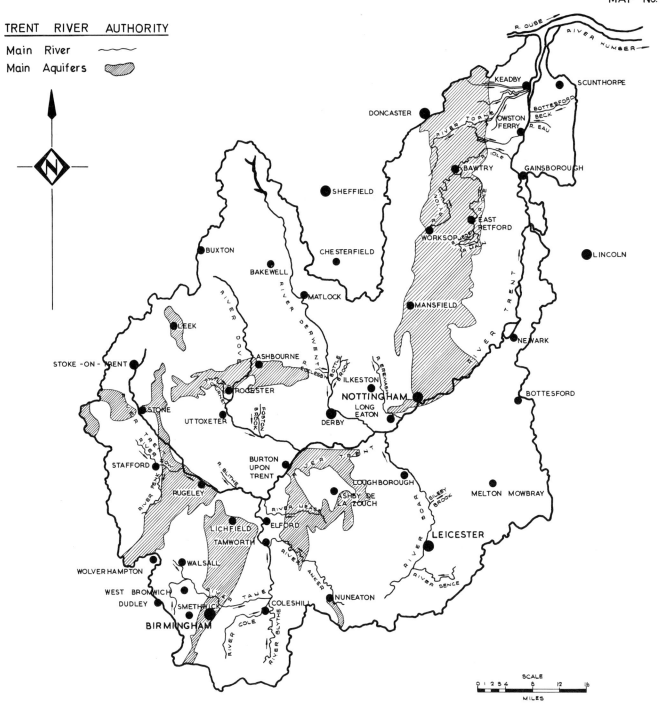

7.6 *Cartoon map of the River Trent basin from which all non-hydrological information has been omitted. (Supplied by the Engineer to the Trent River Authority)*

In addition, better communications, brought about by the railways, the aeroplane, and the telephone, themselves created by engineers, make it possible for this unique concentration of civil engineers to disperse to more amenable working areas.

As at a public enquiry so in a Parliamentary Committee, the engineer and his employer will be made very much aware of public feeling towards their project. Any move to close a railway or road brings forth voluminous and vociferous evidence that the service is operating almost to capacity and that the need is for extra facilities not closure. A remote, infertile valley, when proposed as a reservoir site, becomes a verdant paradise and home of hitherto unrealized cultures.

A Hearing before a Select Parliamentary Committee is similar, in some respects, to a court of law inasmuch as counsel wear wigs and robes and witnesses are under oath.

The case for the promoters is usually presented by learned counsel. It is he who leads the engineer and his expert witnesses through the proofs of evidence in support of the case.

Engineering evidence is supported by many drawings: maps, plans, sections, graphs, etc., copies of which are given to members of the Committee and to the opposition, who scrutinize them in great detail. Any errors or omissions are soon magnified by the opposition counsel.

The promoters of a Bill must be very flexible and capable of turning out clear, authoritative evidence, including drawings, very quickly, overnight if necessary, to meet the sudden turns and developments of the legal argument. Rapid, skilful artists and draughtsmen therefore are essential. (The term Parliamentary draughtsman, incidentally, refers to a specialist lawyer who draws up the phrases of Parliamentary documents.)

A large cartoon, showing the features of the scheme, can be of considerable assistance if hung up in the Committee Room. It helps the sometimes inarticulate engineer to present evidence to the Committee and perhaps strengthens his position against the articulate opposition counsel who may not understand drawings too well.

If the authority is lucky (or rich) enough to retain the most suitable counsel to present its case, the engineer will have more periods of elation than despair during the Hearing. After the Hearing, it is often possible to pinpoint the exact phrase or piece of evidence that turned the case from a doubtful one into a victory for the proposer.

These committees discuss so many diverse aspects of the project that one begins to wonder what connection they all have with engineering. It is salutary to realize what a vast impact engineering has on society and its environment.

The whole, sometimes protracted, business can be frustrating to the engineer who is anxious to get on with the construction of his brainchild. Few engineers however are vain enough to claim that no useful ideas came out of the presentation of their case. Few engineers emerge unchanged from examination by the opposing counsel.

## 7.8 TENDER DRAWINGS

The engineer must decide how much design need be carried out before the Parliamentary stage. Detailed design would be a waste of valuable time as the scheme might be changed out of all recognition. At the same time, enough general or desk design must be carried out so that the engineering difficulties can be evaluated. Witnesses must also have answers ready for all possible questions from the opposition.

Once the legal dust has begun to settle after the Act has been passed and his employers have gone off to find the money to pay for the scheme, the engineer must prepare his first formal set of engineering drawings, the tender drawings. These are the drawings which, together with the other tender documents, bills of quantities, specifications, etc., will describe the scheme to the contractor so that he can price the construction.

Curiously, large schemes often go to tender with fewer drawings and simpler documents than smaller straightforward ones. Two schemes have been known to go to tender with about sixty drawings each, one worth a few tens of thousands of pounds, the other over a hundred million pounds.

The design of small, run of the mill schemes can often be completed in one go. The engineer may have done something similar before and, therefore, stands a reasonable chance of knowing most of the answers in advance. Some slight alterations are to be expected, but may not involve more than half a dozen drawings. With this small type of scheme, the tender drawings, the contract drawings, and perhaps even the record drawings may be the same.

With very large schemes, on the other hand, many of the answers will not be known until the work has started, e.g., until some excavation has been made on a tricky site. Sometimes the sheer volume of drawing office work would occupy too much time and unnecessarily delay tendering. In any case, contractors do not want to be burdened with too much paper and detail when tendering. On the other hand, they must be acquainted with the general principles of the construction, the quantities involved, and the difficulties of the site.

The tender drawings are the first evidence to the world at large of the scale, type, and quality of the scheme involved and, as such, are prepared by many engineers and authori-

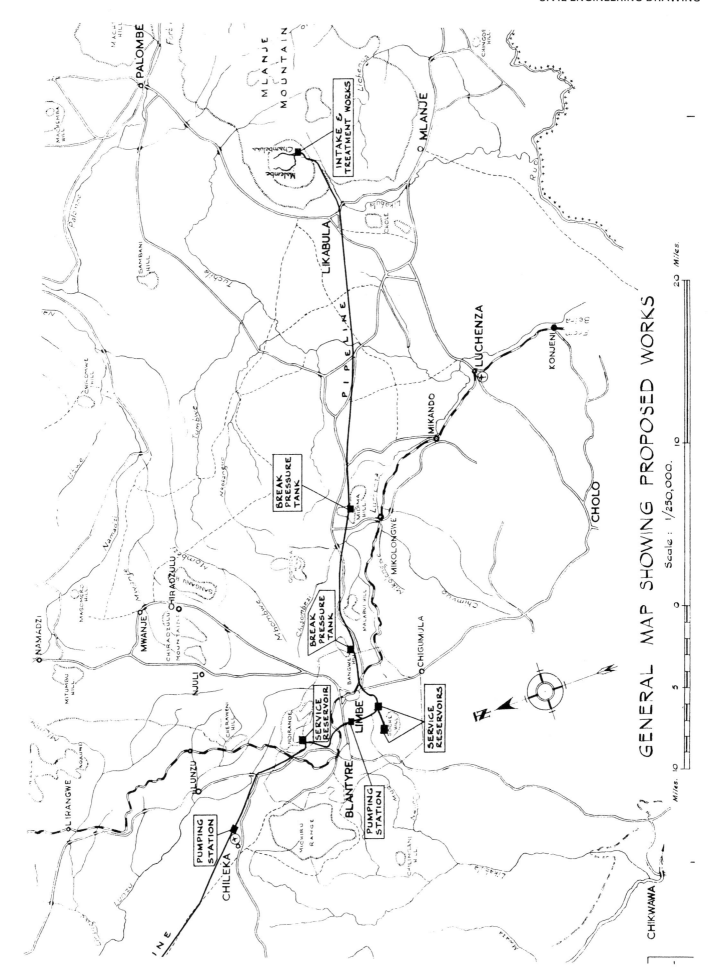

GENERAL MAP SHOWING PROPOSED WORKS

Scale : 1/250,000.

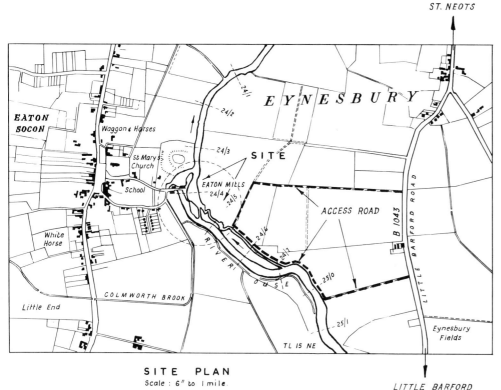

**SITE PLAN**
Scale : 6″ to 1 mile.

7.8 *Site plan of proposed improvement works, showing site access. (Supplied by the Engineer to the Great Ouse River Authority. Eaton Socon Sluice Improvement)*

ties with considerable care, often with particular attention paid to draughting and presentation.

The contractor will hardly be concerned with the prestige value of the drawings to the promoting authority, but he will be concerned with the clarity and logical expression of the engineering detail and its accuracy.

There must be no ambiguity. Probably the only way of ensuring this is to ask an engineer, who has had no previous experience of the scheme, to examine the drawings critically and to say whether he can obtain a clear impression of the scheme and its detail. Junior engineers sometimes feel that their boss is overcritical when he finds faults in something they have worked hard on for weeks. But it is his experienced eye, coming, without preconceived ideas, to the drawing, that has spotted the weaknesses. It is frightening how mistakes or anomalies can escape detection. It can be a salutary experience for any design engineer to have another engineer read and interpret a bar bending

7.7 *1:250 000 map showing the essentials of a recommended scheme for the water supply to two African towns. (Supplied by Scott & Wilson, Kirkpatrick & Partners)*

schedule that he has prepared for a reinforced concrete design, see section 8.3, and to hear his comments afterwards.

Tender drawings can encompass every scale, convention, and concept used in engineering. If the project is hidden away in an obscure corner of the world, the pictorial story can start with a sheet of maps showing all or part of a continent, going on to, *inter alia*, location maps or plans (see Figs. 7.7, 7.9, and 7.10), access plans (see Fig. 7.8), general arrangement drawings (see Fig. 7.11), and finally, drawings with constructional detail (see Figs. 7.12, 7.13, 7.14, and 7.15). Intimate constructional details are included only for smaller or routine schemes. However, all knowledge of the site: borehole logs, geological sections, cross sections and longitudinal sections, closely contoured plans, etc., will be needed, however large or small the job.

## 7.9 CONTRACT DRAWINGS

For several weeks, or months, (if the contractors are fortunate) after the rush of completing the tender drawings and compiling the documents for issue to competing contractors, the engineer will have some respite during which he can carry on with detail design.

During the tendering period, contractors

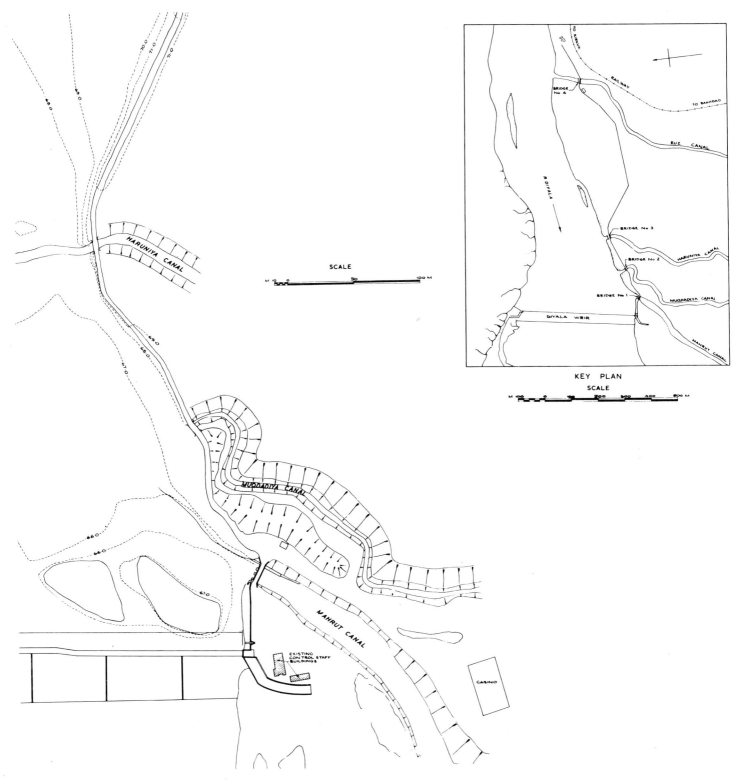

7.9 *Key or location plan of irrigation works in the Middle East, together with part of the site survey to a larger scale. (Supplied by Sir M. MacDonald & Partners)*

7.10 *A continuation of Fig. 7.9. Plan and longitudinal section of the headworks of the irrigation canal, with all relevant data tabulated concisely, accurately, and neatly below the section. (Supplied by Sir M. MacDonald & Partners)*

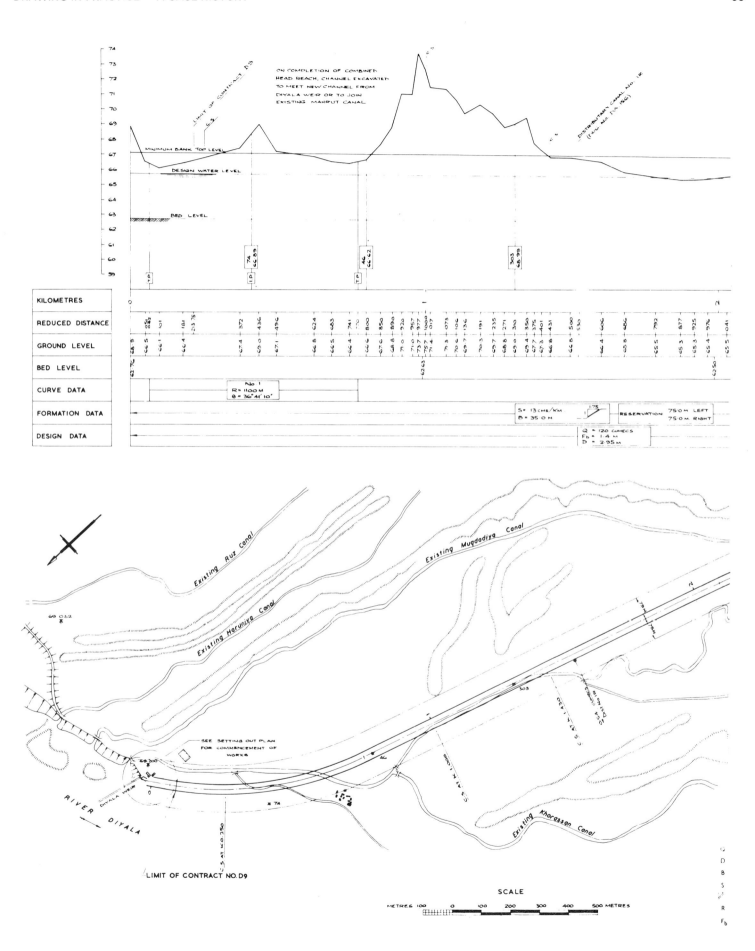

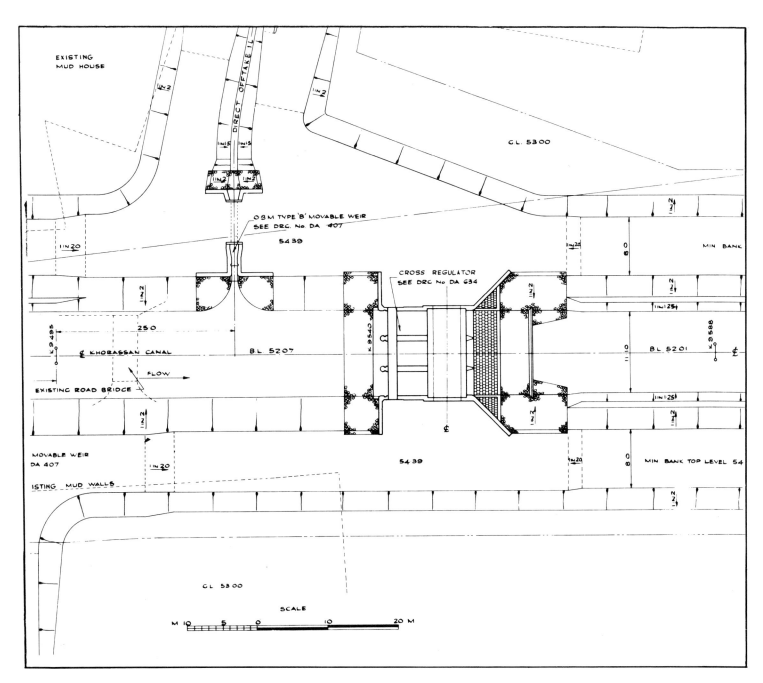

7.11  *General arrangement of a regulator (con-*
      *trol sluice) in an irrigation canal.*
      *(Supplied  by  Sir  M.  MacDonald  &*
      *Partners)*

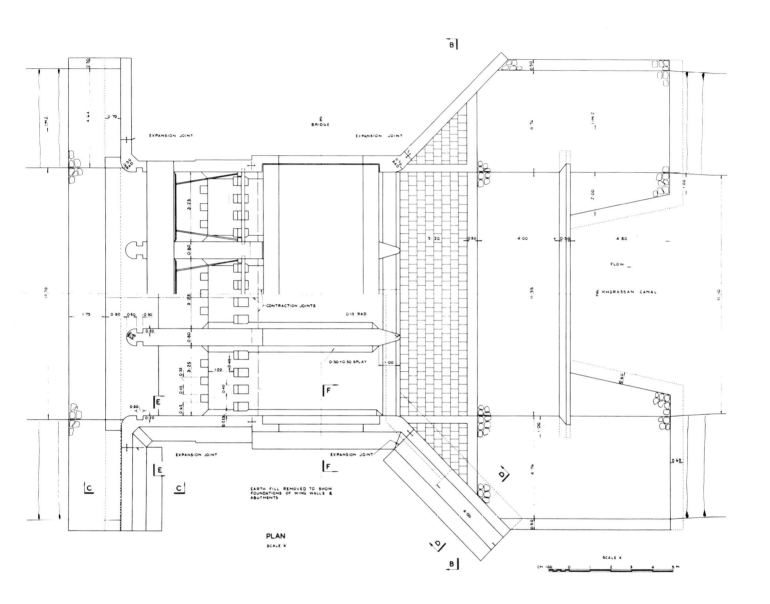

**PLAN**

SCALE 'A'

7.12 *General arrangement of the canal regulator in Fig. 7.11 to a larger scale showing constructional details and dimensions, see also Fig. 7.13. (Supplied by Sir M. MacDonald & Partners)*

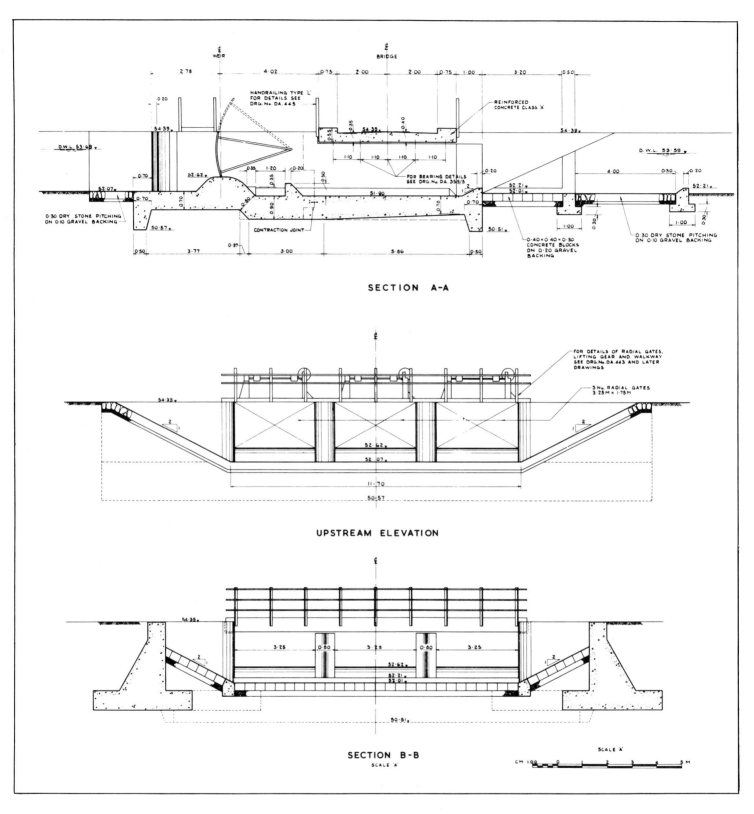

SECTION A-A

UPSTREAM ELEVATION

SECTION B-B
SCALE 'A'

SCALE 'A'

7.13 *Longitudinal section, upstream and downstream elevations of the canal regulator shown in Fig. 7.12. See how the section reveals the construction and layout almost at a glance. (Supplied by Sir M. MacDonald & Partners)*

7.14 *Plan, longitudinal and cross sections of an accommodation (access) bridge over an irrigation canal. The longitudinal section reveals the construction almost at a glance. Notice that Section B-B is distorted. See its alignment on the plan,*

*(Supplied by Sir M. MacDonald & Partners)*

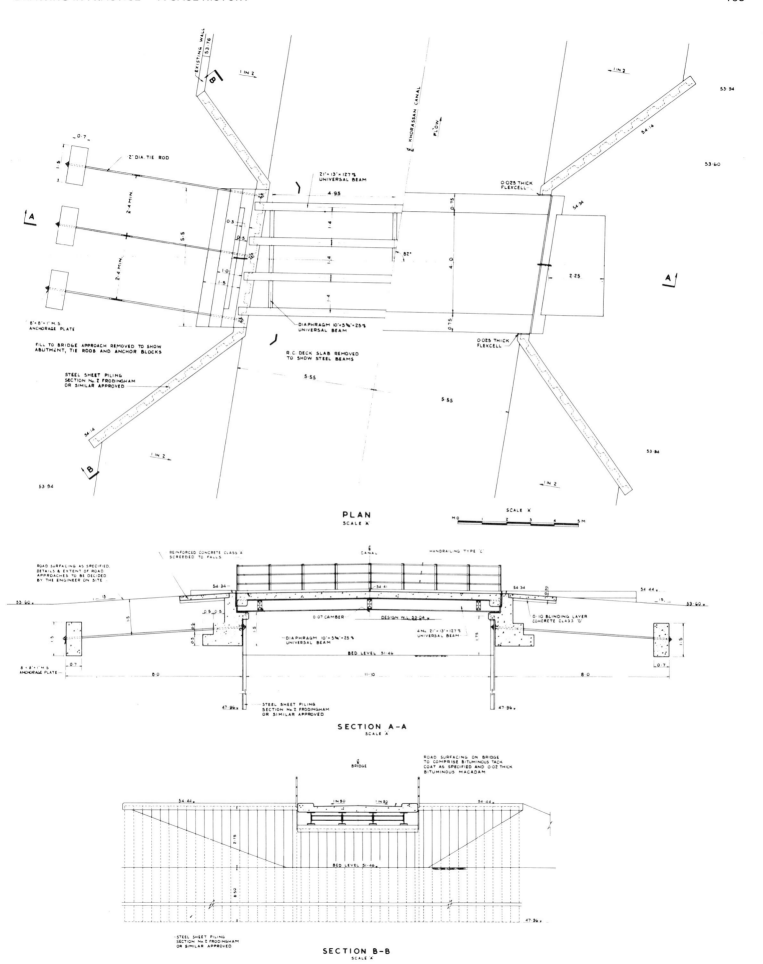

PLAN
SCALE 'A'

SCALE 'A'

SECTION A-A
SCALE 'A'

SECTION B-B
SCALE 'A'

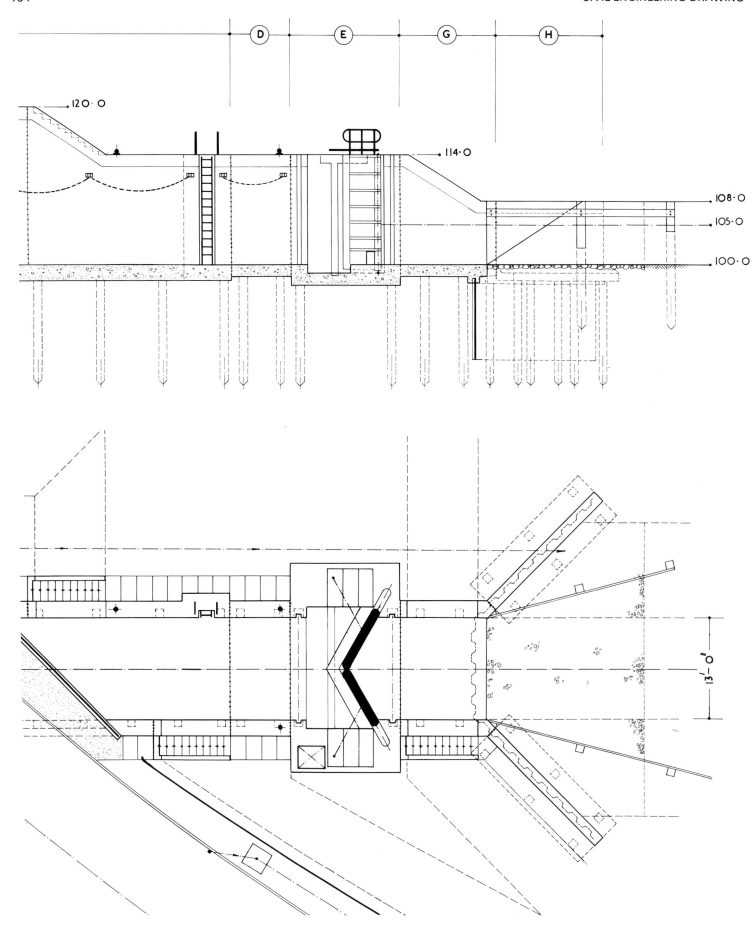

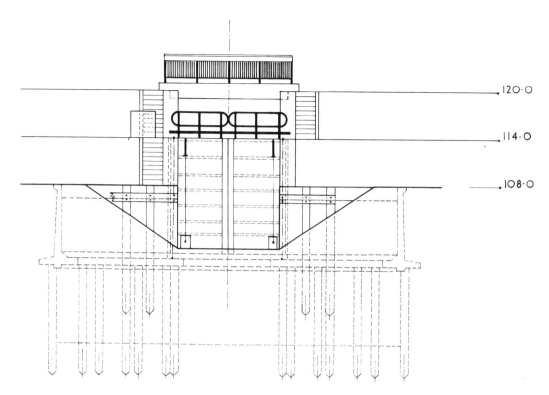

7.15 Detail of a navigation lock.
  (a) Part of the longitudinal section and
      plan from the general arrangement
      of the lock (Supplied by the
      Engineer to the Great Ouse River
      Authority. Hermitage Lock Im-
      provement).
  (b) View from below the lock.
  (c) View from the road bridge.

will be interpreting the tender drawings and preparing their bids. It sometimes happens that one contractor may be skilled in a particular method of construction that is different from that shown in the tender drawings. He may submit a tender based upon his speciality even though it will necessitate an alteration in the design, or even the concept, of the scheme. If his price is competitive and the engineer agrees with his proposals, modified drawings will have to be prepared. The engineer must be flexible in his ideas and realize that there may be better solutions to the problem than his own.

Once the contractors have submitted their tenders, the engineer will have to evaluate and compare them, to look for anomalies in pricing, to see whether the proposed constructional methods are suitable, to see if any legal loopholes have been prized open, etc. On the basis of the engineer's report and recommendation, his employer will accept one of the tenders, for which a legally binding contract will then be prepared, of which the contract drawings form a vital part.

If tendering has been straightforward, the contract drawings will be the same as the tender drawings. If alternative proposals have been accepted, new or additional drawings will have to be prepared.

Contract drawings are usually printed on a linen based paper so that they will survive long storage in the employer's and contractor's archives.

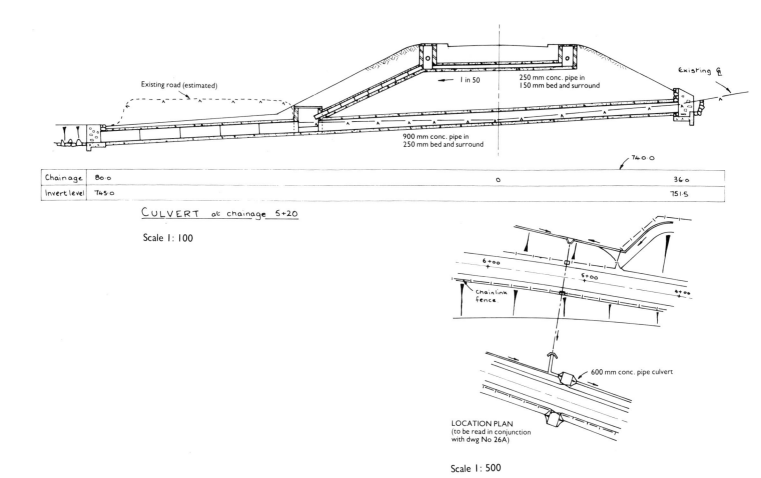

CULVERT at chainage 5+20

Scale 1:100

| Chainage | 80·0 | 0 | 360 |
| Invert level | 745·0 | | 751·5 |

LOCATION PLAN
(to be read in conjunction
with dwg No 26A)

Scale 1:500

*7.16 A working drawing, in pencil on tracing paper, of drainage details of a new road. The drawing was made quickly in a small site office to meet the contractors's construction programme. (Supplied by the Water Engineer, City of Liverpool Water Department)*

## 7.10 WORKING DRAWINGS

The working drawings fill the gaps in the constructional detail left by the general nature of the tender drawings. As the name implies, they are for working or building purposes and must, therefore, represent the engineer's last thoughts on construction. Drastic changes of mind hereafter can be expensive, especially if the contractor is already building and is breathing down the engineer's neck for more detail.

The engineer can sometimes hand over the small routine job to the Resident Engineer on site since the tender drawings contain all the constructional detail. If amendments are small, the site staff can often cope with them, although small contracts may not have sufficient site staff to manage major alterations to drawings.

For the large project, which had only outline drawings at the tender stage, the busiest time for the drawing office lies ahead. The drawing office may be at the engineer's headquarters or it may equally well be on site.

Site or working drawings still need to be complete, accurate, logical, and unambiguous, but the need for prestige completion and presentation has disappeared. The work will probably be left in pencil on tracing paper or polyester film, with notes and instructions written in very freely, but legibly, see Fig. 7.16.

This is perhaps one of the most testing and rewarding aspects of engineering drawing. The engineer knows that the drawing is required urgently, that he must get it right first time, while his working conditions may be anything but ideal.

## 7.11 COMPLETION, RECORD, OR 'AS-BUILT' DRAWINGS

By the very nature of civil engineering, where the engineer is delving into the unknown or partially known recesses of the earth and sometimes designing to the limits of technology, it is unlikely that everything will go literally according to the plan. There is bound to be some alteration or addition to even the very latest working drawing due to some vagary of the site or of the client.

However trifling the deviation from the working drawing, it must be recorded. Every alteration must be recorded on a set of completion or record drawings.

All this work can be accomplished at one sitting for a small job where all has gone well and the engineer in charge is not likely to be whisked away to another job. But for a large project, where each phase or section can take months to complete and be worth millions of pounds, the record drawings must be prepared simultaneously as the work proceeds.

The simplest version of a completion drawing will be a set of prints of the tender or workings drawings duly amended in red ink or pencil. The more involved alteration could well lead to a completely new drawing or set of drawings.

The preparation of completion drawings can be a test of the site engineer's personal concentration and devotion. He may have been left in charge of winding up the job and doing the completion drawings at the same time, when the only real incentive may be to get off the lonely site and back to work on something creative. He should try to realize the value of his work and drawings to the maintenance engineer who, later on, may need to find some buried detail.

## 7.12 ILLUSTRATIONS IN TECHNICAL PAPERS

The final phase in the graphical representation of an engineering project often comes in technical papers. These are published in journals which serve to pass on the useful knowledge gained or new techniques used. This phase may come ten years after the work was first started in the design office.

Unless the paper is to be illustrated by means of full size drawings, which will necessitate the use of unwieldy, expensive, and infuriating pull-out sheets, the drawings will be photographically reduced. Although some designers find albums of the drawings of their previous projects, photographically reduced to about half size (a quarter of the area), are very useful for general reference, much of the detail is lost and notes in the smallest printing are illegible. In any case, too much construction detail is shown on ordinary drawings to be of interest to most readers of technical papers. Even graphs and trend charts need special preparation, cartooning almost, to achieve maximum clarity.

The drawings used to illustrate papers in the *Proceedings of the Institution of Civil Engineers* are a good example of simplified but straightforward technical illustration, see Fig. 7.17. As the small page size of the *Proceedings* restricts illustrations to a width of about 100 mm, a reduction of five or six times is not uncommon. Hence, although authors submit specially made, simplified drawings, the Institution's own draughtsmen usually have to thicken some lines to ensure clarity. Moreover, very thin lines are too frail on the printer's plate which must be capable of printing nearly forty thousand copies. (An offset printing process maintains the clarity of very thin lines better than plates.) Captions are prepared by the Institution to suit the degree of reduction. They are set in type, printed, cut out, and stuck in place on the original drawing, as shown in Fig. 7.17. The smallest acceptable size for lowercase letters on the finished page is about 1 mm high (6 point). For example, for a reduction by five, the captions for the original are prepared in 30 point letters. A whole page of 6 point print would be unacceptable, but isolated notes surrounded by blank paper are clear at this size.

Some journals have developed a stylized technique of their own. For example, the drawings used in *Water Power* are peculiarly and attractively their own, with outlines made up of thick and thin lines which seem to suggest depth and substance in a subtle way.

## 7.13 SLIDES

Slides used to illustrate lectures must be made from specially prepared drawings if they are to have any impact. The overwhelming detail of the typical engineering drawing is confusing, if not completely invisible, on the screen. If in doubt about its suitability as a slide, view the original drawing from a distance comparable with that of an audience at the back of a hall 10 m long viewing a screen 1.5 m wide, and see if all lines and captions are clear, i.e., a drawing 400 mm wide should be viewed from a distance of

$$10 \times \frac{0.4}{1.5} = 2.67 \text{ m},$$

and an A1 drawing from about 5 metres. The thinnest line on a drawing 400 mm wide should be about 0.5 mm thick which, as we saw in section 3.5 which refers to BS 308, gives rise to thick lines a millimetre or more wide—much thicker than the inexperienced

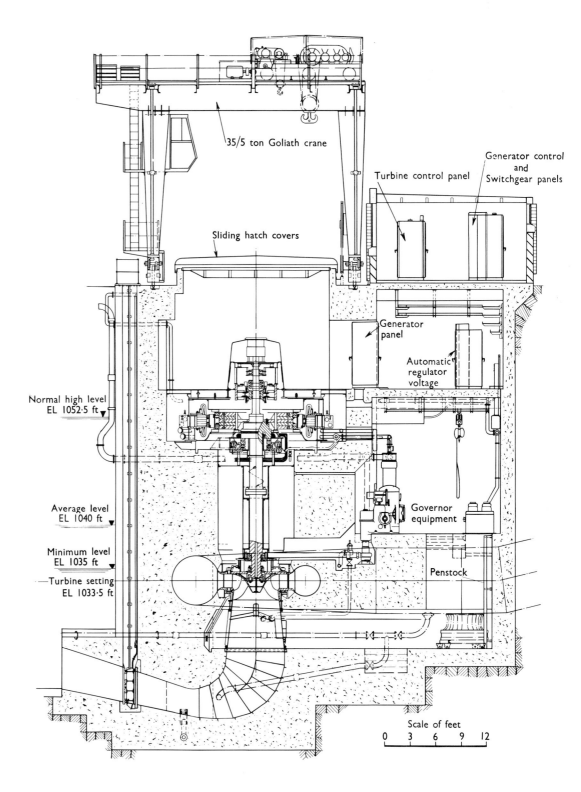

35/5 ton Goliath crane

Generator control
and
Switchgear panels

Turbine control panel

Sliding hatch covers

Generator
panel

Automatic
regulator
voltage

Normal high level
EL 1052·5 ft

Average level
EL 1040 ft

Governor
equipment

Minimum level
EL 1035 ft

Turbine setting
EL 1033·5 ft

Penstock

Scale of feet

0    3    6    9    12

7.17 *Typical section of a hydroelectric power
station, specially prepared for publication in the* Proceedings of The Institution
of Civil Engineers. *(Supplied by the
Institution of Civil Engineers from the
paper* Nkula Falls hydroelectric scheme
initial development *by R. S. Arnott,
D.D.A. Piesold, and J. G. Wiltshire)*

draughtsman would expect. Round, open lettering with bold lines, like the BS 308 example in Fig. 3.11 (a), is clearer than narrower, perhaps more elegant, lettering with considerable variation in line width. Script from most typewriters is unsuitable as the type is thin compared to the size of the letters.

Coloured lines on drawings reproduced on slides present a special problem, since the flood of light on to the screen representing the white background degrades the colours and will almost kill pale colours. Only skilled photographers, with carefully selected colour materials and lighting, can reproduce coloured line work really satisfactorily; the result is so often either quite healthy colours on a dingy blue-grey background or pallid lines on a clear white background.

Some workers prefer to project negative images of line work, i.e., white lines on a dark screen. This can be less tiring to the viewers than a brilliantly lit white screen, but the lecture room is then too dark for making notes without considerable background illumination. Selective colouring of lines is easily achieved by the use of felt or fibre-tipped pens on the emulsion of the slide.

# Chapter 8                   Some specialist applications

*London to Brighton motorway. This motorway is the principal link road to London's Gatwick Airport. (Photograph supplied by R. Travers Morgan, Consulting Engineers, London)*

## 8.1 INTRODUCTION

At the beginning of the present technological age, engineering was either civilian or military. The rapid increase in knowledge during the nineteenth century so diversified the work of the engineer that the electrical and mechanical aspects broke away to diversify even more. This still left the civil engineer with a very wide range of work. The widening of civil engineering itself has continued, until the only common bonds between some of its branches today appear to be mathematics and drawing. Even the latter has developed specialist technologies and applications.

In addition to his fellow specialists, the civil engineer will be working with mechanical, electrical and electronic engineers, not to mention geologists, biologists, chemists, architects, etc.

In this chapter, some examples of specialist applications of drawing are discussed. It is intended only to introduce these topics so that such drawings will give some appreciation of the overall picture of civil engineering.

## 8.2 ARCHITECTURE

### (a) The role of the architect
Popular ideas of the role of the architect cover the extreme ends of the spectrum of his work, but usually leave blank his major role. Some architects are concerned mostly with private dwelling houses, while a few are involved with prestige structures, for example, cathedrals and tower blocks for offices. In the main, architects are concerned with providing the right sort of building for their clients, to which end they must correlate such aspects as planning, landscaping, ergonomics and aesthetics.

**Planning**. Planning means using the site to the client's best advantage within the planning bylaws and restrictions which have been drawn up to prevent exploitation of people and localities by ruthless developers. The overcrowded, back to back housing thrown up in the industrial north during the nineteenth century, or even the straggle of houses along main roads that occurred in the nineteen-thirties, show what can happen if uncontrolled development takes place.

**Landscaping**. Landscaping is concerned with fitting a new scheme into the existing scene as harmoniously as possible, or it could be concerned with creating an attractive environment round an alien structure. As projects become larger and larger, the landscaper is tested more and more. Landscaping need not be expensive, it can be achieved by sympathetic attention to detail.

**Ergonomics**. Ergonomics is concerned with making the building fit the people who will inhabit it, in respect of both comfort and efficiency, whether the building is for domestic or industrial purposes.

**Aesthetics**. Aesthetics are concerned with providing a tasteful building or environment that fulfills its function efficiently. There is an obvious connection here with landscaping. Nothing can hide the vast electricity generating stations that must spread across the country as we demand more power, but if care is taken in locating the 120 m high cooling towers and the 200 m high chimneys, the effect is less disastrous. The present trend, introduced for technological reasons, of using one larger multiple chimney rather than several smaller ones, creates a less fussy outline.

Architects are popularly supposed to be weak in the field of structural design while engineers reputedly have philistine views and inferior aesthetic ability. Even though generalisations, these notions are unfortunately true to

*8.1 Block plan. Scale 1:500.*

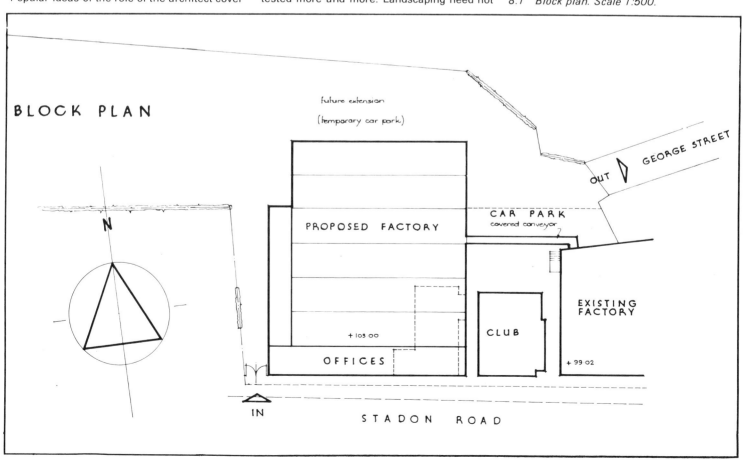

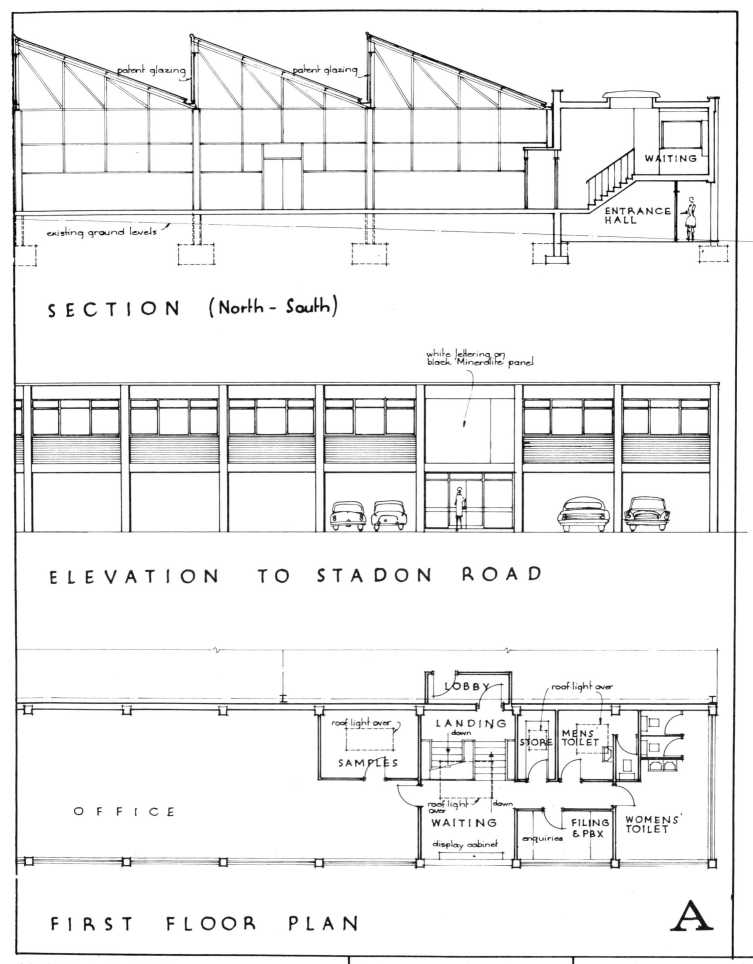

SECTION (North - South)

patent glazing · patent glazing

WAITING

ENTRANCE HALL

existing ground levels

white lettering on black 'Mineralite' panel

ELEVATION TO STADON ROAD

FIRST FLOOR PLAN

LOBBY

roof-light over

roof-light over

LANDING
down

STORE

MENS TOILET

SAMPLES

OFFICE

roof-light over

down

WAITING

display cabinet

enquiries

FILING & PBX

WOMENS' TOILET

A

Scale: 1:100

Francis W. Keyworth, L.B.I.B.
Chartered Architect,

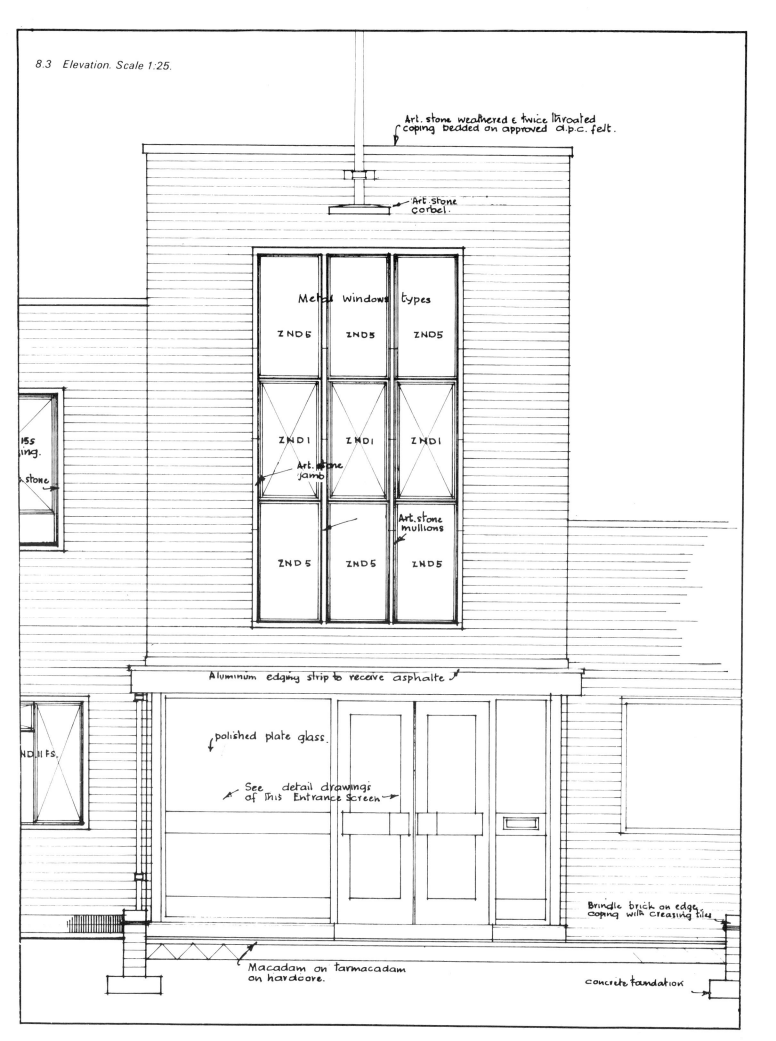

8.3 Elevation. Scale 1:25.

Art. stone weathered & twice throated
coping bedded on approved d.p.c. felt.

Art. stone corbel.

Metal windows types

ZND5    ZND5    ZND5

ZND1    ZND1    ZND1

Art. stone jamb

Art. stone mullions

ZND5    ZND5    ZND5

Aluminium edging strip to receive asphalte

polished plate glass.

See detail drawings
of this Entrance Screen

ND II FS.

155
sing.

stone

Brindle brick on edge
coping with creasing tiles

Macadam on tarmacadam
on hardcore.

concrete foundation

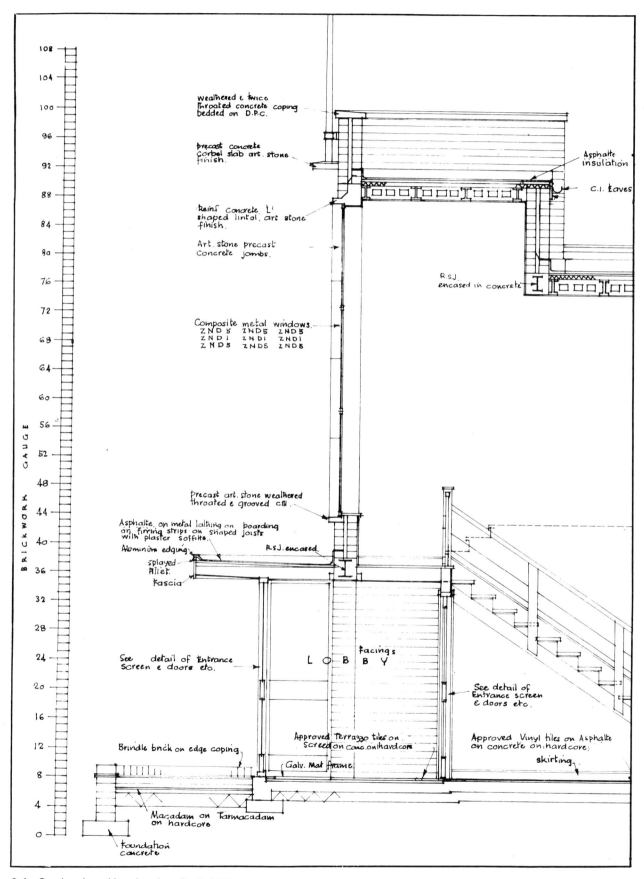

BRICKWORK GAUGE

108
104
100
96
92
88
84
80
76
72
68
64
60
56
52
48
44
40
36
32
28
24
20
16
12
8
4
0

Weathered & twice throated concrete coping bedded on D.P.C.

Precast concrete corbel slab art. stone finish.

Reinf concrete L shaped lintol art stone finish.

Art. stone precast concrete jambs.

Composite metal windows.
ZND 5  ZND 5  ZND 5
ZND 1  ZND 1  ZND 1
ZND 5  ZND 5  ZND 5

Precast art. stone weathered throated & grooved cill.

Asphalte on metal lathing on boarding on firring strips on shaped joists with plaster soffite.

Aluminium edging.

Splayed fillet.

Fascia

See detail of Entrance screen & doors etc.

Brindle brick on edge coping.

Macadam on Tarmacadam on hardcore

Foundation concrete

Asphalte insulation

C.I. Eaves

R.S.J. encased in concrete

R.S.J. encased

LOBBY  Facings

See detail of Entrance screen & doors etc.

Approved Terrazzo tiles on screed on conc. on hardcore

Galv. Mat frame.

Approved Vinyl tiles on Asphalte on concrete on hardcore.

skirting.

8.4   Sectional working drawing. Scale 1:25.

some extent. The better architects and engineers do complement each other, while the best could perform each other's tasks. Two good heads are always better than one; the philosophical and technological interchange of ideas between architect and engineer, arguing from different viewpoints, will always benefit a job.

Students of civil engineering should not forget that design is aesthetic and ergonomic as well as structural. It is concerned as much with appearance and convenience as with sizes of structural members and the stress in them.

Whether the engineer employs the architect or *vice versa* depends largely on the content of the job. If it is essentially building (in the wider sense, not dwelling houses), the architect will have overall control and will call in structural and service engineers to advise and carry out their part of the design. Bridges, dams, power stations, motorways, etc., are engineering projects which need the advice of an architect to make them fit into their environment. Even a simple roadway cutting can benefit from landscaping.

### (b) Architects' drawings

The architect builds up his designs in the same reasoned and logical way as the engineer. He starts by outlining the building on 1:100 or smaller sketch plans, which are correct scale drawings and include elevations and sections, see Fig. 8.2. The text indicates the scale ratios.

The sketch plans enable him to prepare the 1:500 scale block plans, see Fig. 8.1. required to obtain outline planning approval, i.e. to discover whether the scheme can go ahead or not.

Further work leads on to 1:25 scale detail drawings which should reveal most of the snags and provide constructional working drawings, see Fig. 8.3 and Fig. 8.4.

Final planning approval on appearance, etc., is now obtained.

Construction is sometimes carried out from heavily annotated 1:100 scale drawings, but this places considerable reliance on the building contractor and his craftsmen. This frequently causes delays on site while the architect is contacted to sort out a problem and can result in expensive remedial work on detail not revealed by the small drawings.

Perhaps the most outstanding difference between an architect's drawings and an engineer's is the realism the former obtains by the clever use of lines of different thickness and close attention to detail, i.e., double lines, however fine, to show door and window frames, shadows etc. His buildings seem related to their surroundings and firmly attached to the ground, helped by figures, trees, vehicles and other detail however representational.

Architects do not achieve realism in their drawings any more easily than engineers do. The apparent sloppiness of some architectural drawings is misleading. There is usually an economy and clever use of line, gained only through experience and practice. Economy of line is not leaving out lines at random, but knowing which ones to leave out.

### 8.3 DETAILING REINFORCED CONCRETE

### (a) Introduction

This section is not concerned with stress analysis and the design of reinforced concrete, but with the clear and concise presentation of its details in drawings.

In view of the complexity of reinforced concrete structures and the very wide range of bar shapes that can arise, it is essential that presentation is standardised.

Standardisation is required both in drawings and in the bar bending schedules needed for ordering the reinforcement, and for the identification of the steel on site.

For any reinforced concrete structure, the draughtsman must provide:

(a) a dimensional layout which gives all the dimensions required to form the structure; cross references must be made on this drawing to the concrete specifications for the structure,

(b) a reinforcing steel drawing,

(c) a bar bending schedule.

8.5  *Reinforcement drawing in accordance with the report,* The Detailing of Reinforced Concrete.

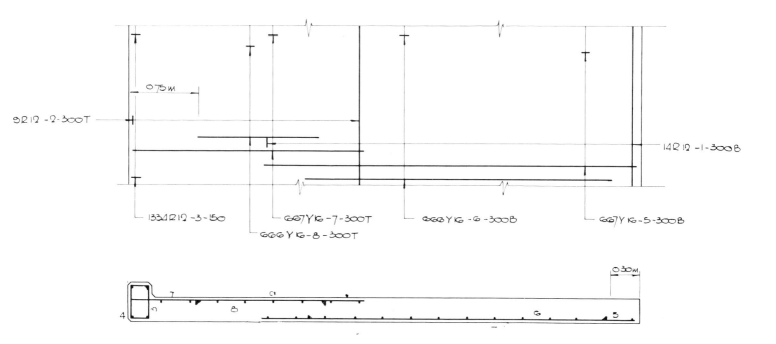

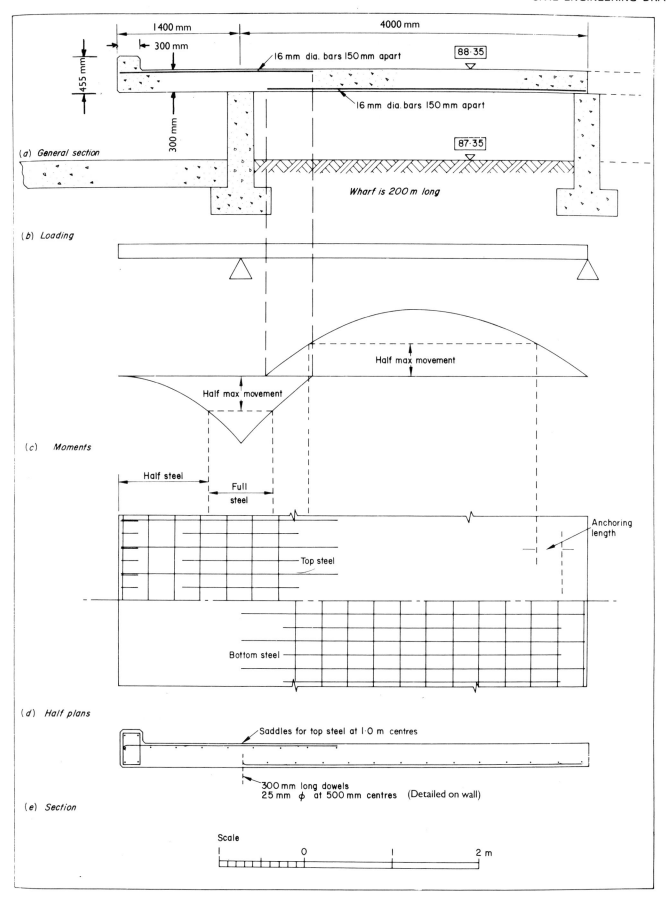

8.6   A reinforced concrete loading wharf.
(a) General section showing theoretical reinforcement required.
(b) Loading.
(c) Envelope of bending moments for reinforcement design.
(d) Half plans showing steel in the top and the bottom of the slab.
(e) Section showing arrangement of the reinforcement as placed.

| Member | Bar mark | Type and size | No. of mbrs | No. of bars in each | Total no. | Length of each bar † mm | Shape code | A * mm | B * mm | C * mm | D * mm | E/r * mm |
|---|---|---|---|---|---|---|---|---|---|---|---|---|
| Wharf Slab | 1 | R12 | 1 | 12 | 12 | 1995 | 20 | 1995 | | | | |
| | 2 | R12 | 1 | 7 | 7 | 1995 | 20 | 1995 | | | | |
| | 3 | R12 | 1 | 1334 | 1334 | 1120 | 60 | 190 | 350 | | | |
| | 4 | R12 | 1 | 4 | 4 | 1995 | 20 | 1995 | | | | |
| | 5 | Y16 | 1 | 667 | 667 | 4000 | 20 | 4000 | | | | |
| | 6 | Y16 | 1 | 666 | 666 | 3350 | 20 | 3350 | | | | |
| | 7 | Y16 | 1 | 667 | 667 | 2650 | 32 | 2500 | | | | |
| | 8 | Y16 | 1 | 666 | 666 | 1350 | 20 | 1350 | | | | |
| | 9 | R16 | 1 | 201 | 201 | 1000 | 83 | 200 | 200 | 200 | 200 | |

XY and partners
Site ref : Job number 1234
Physics block, Eastford

Bar schedule ref: 0 4 6 0 3 A   Rev letter
Date prepared 8.6.80 Date revised. 31.9.80
Prepared by. A.B.C   Checked by. D.E.F

A

This schedule complies with the requirements of BS 4466
*Specified in multiples of 5 mm.      † Specified in multiples of 25 mm.

8.7  Bar schedule.

The preparation of dimensional layouts for a structure is straightforward and needs no special treatment. It should however be emphasised that all information necessary for the construction of the structure, other than details of the reinforcing steel, must be provided on this drawing.

Preparation of reinforcing steel drawings should be in accordance with the publication *Standard Methods of Detailing Reinforced Concrete*. The scheduling of reinforcing steel should be in accordance with BS 4466: 1981.

Reinforcing steel is available in several forms and the type used must be noted on the drawing. The forms available are:

(a) Hot rolled mild steel bars to BS 4449
(b) Hot rolled high yield bars to BS 4449
(c) Cold worked steel bars to BS 4461
(d) Steel fabric for the reinforcement of concrete to BS 4453.

Mild steel bars are available as either plain or deformed. Deformed bars form a better bond with the concrete. Hot rolled high yield bars are only available as deformed bars and cold worked steel bars are square, twisted, high yield bars. Reinforcing steel is available in the following sizes: 6, 8, 10, 12, 16, 20, 25, 32, and 40 mm. Fifty millimetre bars are also available.

Actual sizes of deformed or twisted bars are greater than the nominal bar diameter by up to 13% and this must be taken into account in the case of heavily reinforced sections.

On reinforcing drawings, mild steel bars are differentiated from high yield bars as:

R12 – 12 mm ø mild steel bar
Y20 – 20 mm ø high yield bar.

The design of reinforcing steel should be in accordance with CP 110, *The Structural Use of Concrete* – Parts 1, 2 and 3. Part 1 – *Design, Materials and Workmanship*, covers provisions for minimum areas of steel, rules for curtailment of steel beyond the area in which it is required and other factors governing design. The reinforcing steel in Fig. 8.6 has been designed in accordance with the provisions of this code. Some points to note are:

(a) Reinforcement has been curtailed in areas of reduced bending moment.
(b) With the greatly improved bond of deformed bars, hooks should only be used where it is necessary to hook one set of bars around another.
(c) Distribution steel has been provided in the direction normal to the main steel. This allows the slab to redistribute stresses laterally, to resist thermal stres-

8.8 *A reinforcing mat of thin bars (about 10 mm in diameter) tied by using a special tool and prepared lengths of soft iron wire. Often plain wire is used and cut to length as needed. The wire is then tied by skilful use of pincers. (Photograph supplied by the Cement and Concrete Association)*

ses. It also enables the steel fixer to maintain the design spacing.

(d) The upstand at the left-hand end has been reinforced with rectangular stirrups which also support the main reinforcement.
(e) Dowels have been provided to prevent the slab moving on the front supporting wall due to thermal creep or vibration. (Other methods, such as keyways in the top of the wall would do as well.)
(f) No reinforcement is placed within 40 mm of the surface of the concrete, this is known as the cover. Steel at the bottom of the slab is laid on small concrete blocks 40 mm thick and about 40 mm square. Top steel is carried on chairs to shape Code 83 of BS 4466.
(g) All main reinforcement is carried past the point where it is no longer required to carry tensile loads.

Figure 8.5 shows the reinforcement for a simple wharf slab, detailed in accordance with the *Standard Methods of Detailing Reinforced Concrete*.

The necessary information will appear on two separate drawings. Figure 8.5 shows the arrangement of the reinforcement. Notice here that no slab dimensions are given; only one bar of each type is shown fully; bars in the top and bottom of the slab are shown as full lines; and the quantity of each bar is shown once only. Figure 8.7 shows a portion of a bar schedule which would be completed by the draughtsman in accordance with the reinforcement design and the 'Shape Code' of the preferred shapes, measurement, specification and length calculation as described in BS 4466. The bar schedule is very important and is complete in itself in order that the contractor can send it to his own yard for the steel to be ordered and bent, without reference to any other drawing.

The steel fixers on site require both the drawing and the schedule. The drawing tells them where and how to locate the bars, while the bar schedule tells them the shapes of the bars.

The steel fixers tie each intersection with soft iron wire. This is one good reason for using the largest bars possible to reduce the number and thus the time and cost of fixing them, see Fig. 8.8.

An example is given in Fig. 8.5 which shows a simple cantilevered loading wharf for lorries. The reinforcing bars of circular section mild steel, theoretically necessary to carry the tensile forces in the slab, are shown as heavy lines on the general section (a). A practical layout of the reinforcement is shown in section (e) and by means of half plans (d).

What conventions have been observed in the reinforcement drawing?

(a) Reinforcement is shown by single, thick, out of scale lines that stand out clearly from all other detail. End views of bars can be made even more out of scale if necessary to show them more clearly.

(b) Slab dimensions are not shown in views which detail reinforcement.

(c) Location dimensions for the ends of bars are restricted to the section where possible.

(d) Conventional concrete shading is not used on the section. (A light pencil shading on sections, applied to the back of tracings, makes sections stand out on prints.)

(e) No attempt is made in the section to separate bars in the same horizontal plane.

(f) The first bar in a series is shown whole in plan and a short bit of the last one, but no others. A thin line at right angle to the bars with an arrowhead to the whole bar and the fragment carries a reference, for which the preferred form is: 20R8–63–150T, which means: 20 bars of round mild steel (R), 8 mm diameter, bar mark 63 at 150 mm centres in the Top of the slab.

The number of bars in each group should be given on the drawing only once, to avoid confusion when totalling on the schedule.

In the section, a bar mark is written parallel to the main reinforcing bars if there is no ambiguity, otherwise an arrow is used to connect the reference uniquely to the bar. The references for longitudinal bars are written normal to the slab, if possible, close to the actual bar or indicated by arrows if necessary.

The bar mark is the unique reference of a bar within the job. On small jobs, the types of bar can be numbered from mark 1 onwards. On larger projects, bars can be numbered sequentially for each structure, e.g., bars for a sluice

are marked S1 onwards, while bars for a bridge are marked B1 onwards. Bars can also be scheduled for each drawing, so long as each bar in the whole job has a unique reference. This is usually done by including the drawing number in the reference.

It is not normally recommended that bars be shown by broken lines. It is preferable to use full lines for all bars detailed on the drawing, broken lines are for bars detailed on another drawing.

(b) Standardisation

Even this simple example shows what a time-consuming job the detailing of reinforcement can become. The work is difficult to check moreover and errors in reinforcement cause delays on site. Standardisation is therefore essential to limit the degree of error.

Further standardisation can be adopted within drawing offices concerned with repetitive structural work. Standard sections for beams, columns, pile caps, etc., should be adopted. Pre-printed, out-of-scale A4 size drawings of these units, requiring only a length and bar size and spacing to be written in by office staff, rather than draughtsmen, can be used.

## 8.4 DETAILING STEELWORK

Steelwork is less of a puzzle, in some ways, to the lay observer than reinforced concrete because there can be occasions when less of it is hidden. Nearly every part of a roof truss in a garage or warehouse can be seen and, apart from the deck construction, the details of a bridge can be taken in if you walk across.

The famous product of the Industrial Revolution, the iron bridge over the River Severn at Ironbridge, in Coalbrookdale, a few miles from Shrewsbury, is worth a visit. It shows how the craft of the timber joiner was cleverly applied to early construction in iron. Inspection of the roofs of nineteenth century railway stations shows the many different members and sections used by the pioneers of iron and steel.

### (a) BS 4 and safe load tables

As ideas and design procedures crystallised and steel rolling techniques improved, it became possible, and later economically necessary, to limit and improve the range of standard steel sections. These are scheduled in BS 4 which shows the geometric dimensions and properties of the larger universal beams.

BS 4 makes no reference to strength. The increase in working strength of structural steel

is reflected in the safe load tables published from time to time by the British Constructional Steelwork Association. Some manufacturers issue the identical tables between their own covers as promotional literature.

### (b) Hollow sections

Several famous railway bridges, erected in the last century, have rivetted hollow sections. The Forth Railway Bridge, for example, has enormous circular hollow sections in compression, while the Saltash Bridge uses large oval sections as tied arches. The solution of the shaping and jointing problems involved in these early uses of hollow sections was expensive. As a result, the hollow section fell from favour until modern gas cutting and automatic welding processes became available, giving the additional advantage of prefabrication.

Large, hollow elements, frequently trapezoidal in section, can be used to create clear, pleasing structures. The hollow section can be sealed to prevent atomspheric corrosion of the inside while the simple flat outside faces are easy to maintain, see Fig. 8.9.

Because they can be of an aerodynamic shape, hollow sections have a greater aesthetic appeal, at the same time considerably reducing wind resistance.

### (c) Composite construction

The high tensile strength of steel is sometimes used to complement the compressive strength of concrete, as shown in Fig. 8.10 and Fig. 8.11. The concrete deck gives some weather protection to the steel tension element below, while its mass and rigidity both stabilise the structure and transmit lateral loads to the supports.

### (d) Fixings

The elements of structural steelwork can be joined, or connected in four ways. These are, in the historical order of their development, by using bolts, by using rivets, by welding and by using friction grip bolts.

Bolts. Bolts may be black or high tensile. Black bolts are cheap fixings because they are mass produced and remain untreated.

High tensile bolts are made of stronger material with more care taken during manufacture. Neither black bolts nor high tensile ones have any control over the tension or grip they develop on the joint. They must be tight without being overstrained. Their action is almost certain to be in shear (after the completed joint has moved fractionally under load).

Bolts can be turned and fitted (driven often with a large hammer) into accurately reamed holes if movement of a joint must be reduced or almost prevented.

**Rivets**. Rivets, still used satisfactorily in some shop manufacture, are no longer used on site as the provision of adequate control is difficult and expensive. They are inserted hot into holes, held in alignment by 'tacking' bolts, and are then hammered or squeezed until the plain end is formed into another head. Well-fitted rivets almost completely fill their holes and, if made absolutely tight when still very hot, they tighten the joint as they cool and shrink. Their action again is mostly in shear with perhaps less movement of the joint than with bolts because the rivet should fill the clearance in its hole.

**Welding**. Welding allows a neat edge to edge abutment of structural sections with few straps or gusset plates. This gives rise to simpler smoother structures requiring simpler drawings.

**Friction grip bolts**. Friction grip bolts overcome many of the drawbacks of the previous fixings and, in addition, can be used by semi-skilled labour. The strength of the joint comes from the friction developed between the structural members when pinched together in a controlled manner. The pinching load is found by determining the extension of the special high tensile steel bolt by controlling the tightening of its nut on special washers. The tightening of the nut is controlled either by torque or, more crudely, by counting the number of turns of the nut after it has become tight. The torque is usually controlled by torque wrenches, which slip after a predetermined torque has been achieved on the nut.

**(e) Drawings**

The leading dimensions of a structure, as determined by the architect (for buildings, etc.) or the engineer (for bridges, etc.) are normally presented to the designer on a small scale drawing, about 1:100.

The designer will determine loads and stresses in the members so that a detailer can prepare a working plan which shows sections and weights in enough detail for competing contractors to tender a price for the work.

Shop fabrication and site construction will follow more detailed drawings, as large as 1:10 scale. Every member is drawn out, as the entire design is the responsibility of the engineer and his team who should not rely on the workshop or the site to attend to details.

Normal orthographic projection is used. Dotted lines are used to show important hidden detail. Sometimes only one view, say an elevation, is shown of a member, perhaps a beam, if it is a standard section with a simple pattern of holes to be drilled, that can be described adequately by simple notes.

Bolts and rivets are shown by + on drawings, with a note, usually in the lower right-hand corner, specifying the fixing, whether it is shop or site fitted, whether it is a rivet or a bolt, whether it is friction bolt or not. Some offices, however, denote rivets by + and bolts by O.

8.9 *Kaiserhain Bridge, Dortmund, Germany, showing the clean, easily maintained shapes that can be created with welded hollow sections. (Photograph supplied by the British Constructional Steelwork Association)*

BS 499, *Welding Terms and Symbols*, gives a comprehensive list of preferred symbols and notation for welding instructions, which are being adopted by some designers. Some of these symbols are used in Fig. 8.12.

Fig 8.13 is a working drawing of a portal frame of built-up welded hollow section.

## 8.5 SURVEYING

### (a)  The engineer as surveyor

The repetitive, time-consuming toil involved in very large surveys is now almost a thing of the past. The days are over when surveyors disappeared into desert or moutainous regions for long periods with armies of guides, chainmen, labourers, cooks, etc. For one thing, there are not so many completely unmapped areas of the world left. Moreover, most of those that remain can be surveyed so much more quickly and cheaply from the air, see Fig. 8.14. What unknown techniques has the civil engineer or surveyor yet to inherit from government departments which claim that they can take worthwhile photographs of military ground installations from aeroplanes flying in the sub-stratosphere or from satellites orbiting the earth hundreds of miles up?

Whatever new techniques develop for surveying whole continents, the engineer will always be faced with tape, level and theodolite exercises for preparing site plans with sufficient detail, for locating structures, and to take off quantities for payment.

### (b) Plotting surveys

In the previous pages, drawings have, in the main, been fully detailed and that includes all the necessary dimensions to enable the subject to be manufactured, without recourse to the taking of dimensions from the drawing by scaling. Hence these drawings need not be redrawn if subsequently some dimensions are altered.

Survey drawings are different. Very few dimensions will appear and any measurements will have to be taken from the drawing itself. For this reason alone, the drawing must be accurately plotted to scale, and this means a good quality drawing medium must be used, one which is not subject to any excessive change in length with any change in temperature or humidity. In particular it should not stretch or shrink on one axis more than another, and so distort angles.

For serious and important work, plastic film will probably fulfil most of the above conditions. However for general work, a good quality cartridge paper should be used as it may have to endure a lot of rubbing out. It should have a smooth surface that will take ink.

However stable paper is, it will shrink or stretch a bit, so all the survey stations to be plotted on the sheet should be located in one session, as quickly as possible, i.e., all computations should be completed before starting the plotting. Plotting of detail from traverse lines between stations can be carried out later, piecemeal if necessary, and will be less affected by paper variations.

Pencils should be 3H and must be kept very sharp. Conical pencil points or divider points should be used for pricking off dimensions on the paper straight from the scale; never transfer measurements with dividers. Chisel points should be used for drawing traverse lines. The pencil point must be used as closely as possible to the straightedge or set square, the line being almost invisible until the straightedge has been removed from the paper.

The only pieces of special equipment required for plotting surveys are:

(a) Beam compasses for swinging large arcs.

(b) Long straightedges of steel, wood, or plastic for drawing the traverse lines. These are longer and more accurate than tee squares and should be used only for plotting surveys and similar draughting work.

### (c) Methods of surveying and plotting

Every survey is based upon a number of stations which are located as accurately as the chosen method of survey allows. The methods adopted will be determined primarily by the accuracy required. This choice, however, will be modified to some extent by the site itself, whether it is level and whether access to all parts is easy or even possible.

The survey stations are joined by traverse lines to which topographical detail can be referenced by offsets.

It is very important to remember that the accuracy of the survey plot must reflect the accuracy of the survey itself.

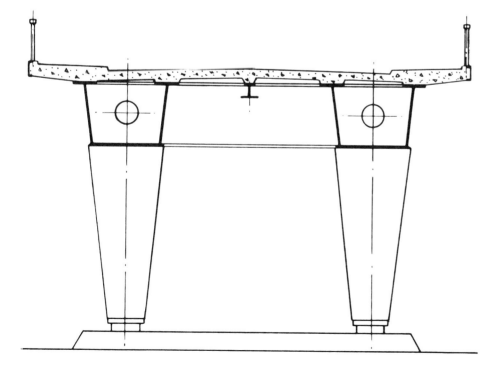

*8.10 Composite construction. Cross section of a type design for a motorway overbridge. Note the trapezoidal welded steel hollow section, shown in heavy lines. The deck is a reinforced concrete slab. (Supplied by the British Constructional Steelwork Association)*

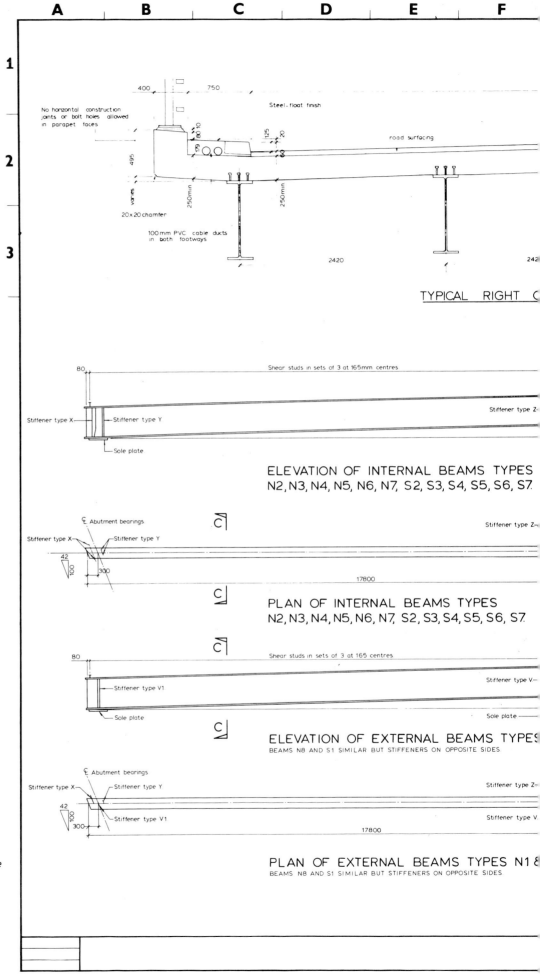

**Top section labels (grid):** A  B  C  D  E  F

No horizontal construction joints or bolt holes allowed in parapet faces

400     750

Steel-float finish

road surfacing

495

125   20

250min     250min

varies

20×20 chamfer

100mm PVC cable ducts in both footways

2420          242

TYPICAL  RIGHT  C

80          Shear studs in sets of 3 at 165mm centres

Stiffener type Z-

Stiffener type X ── ── Stiffener type Y

Sole plate

## ELEVATION OF INTERNAL BEAMS TYPES
### N2, N3, N4, N5, N6, N7, S2, S3, S4, S5, S6, S7.

℄ Abutment bearings

Stiffener type X ── Stiffener type Y

Stiffener type Z-

42
100
300

17800

## PLAN OF INTERNAL BEAMS TYPES
### N2, N3, N4, N5, N6, N7, S2, S3, S4, S5, S6, S7.

80          Shear studs in sets of 3 at 165 centres

Stiffener type V1

Stiffener type V-

Sole plate     Sole plate

## ELEVATION OF EXTERNAL BEAMS TYPES
BEAMS N8 AND S1 SIMILAR BUT STIFFENERS ON OPPOSITE SIDES.

℄ Abutment bearings

Stiffener type X ──     Stiffener type Y

Stiffener type Z-

42
100
300          Stiffener type V1

Stiffener type V.

17800

## PLAN OF EXTERNAL BEAMS TYPES N1 &
BEAMS N8 AND S1 SIMILAR BUT STIFFENERS ON OPPOSITE SIDES.

*8.11 Detail drawing for a composite beam and slab bridge deck. (Supplied by Sir William Halcrow and Partners)*

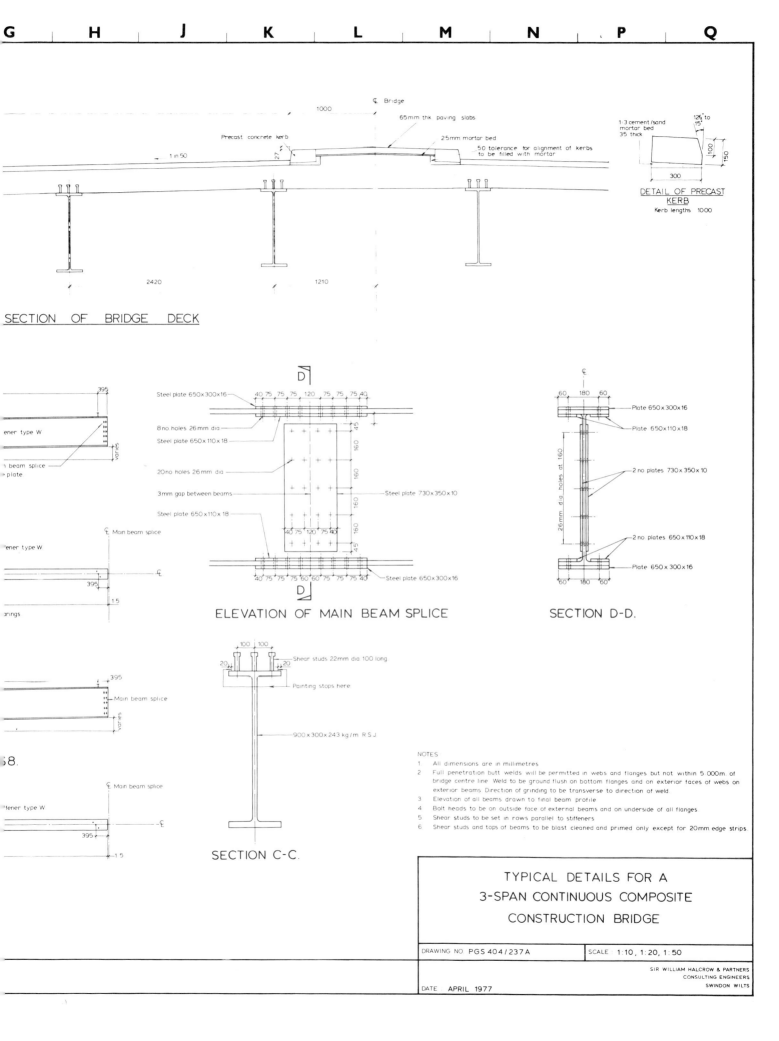

G H J K L M N P Q

**SECTION OF BRIDGE DECK**

€ Bridge
1000
65mm thk paving slabs
Precast concrete kerb
25mm mortar bed
50 tolerance for alignment of kerbs to be filled with mortar
1 in 50
27
2420   1210

1:3 cement /sand mortar bed 35 thick
12½° to 15°
100
150
300

**DETAIL OF PRECAST KERB**
Kerb lengths 1000

fener type W
395
m beam splice plate
varies

fener type W
€ Main beam splice
395
€
1 5
arings

395
Main beam splice
varies

58.

fener type W
€ Main beam splice
395
€
1 5

**ELEVATION OF MAIN BEAM SPLICE**

D
Steel plate 650×300×16
40 75 75 75 120 75 75 75 40
8 no holes 26 mm dia
Steel plate 650×110×18
45
160
20 no holes 26 mm dia
160
3mm gap between beams
160
Steel plate 730×350×10
Steel plate 650×110×18
160
40 75 120 75 40
45
Steel plate 650×300×16
40 75 75 75 60 60 75 75 75 40
D

**SECTION D-D.**

€
60 180 60
Plate 650 × 300×16
Plate 650 × 110×18
26 mm dia holes at 160
2 no plates 730×350×10
2 no plates 650×110×18
Plate 650 × 300×16
60 180 60

**SECTION C-C.**

100 100
20 20
Shear studs 22mm dia 100 long
Painting stops here
900 × 300 × 243 kg/m R S J

**NOTES**
1   All dimensions are in millimetres
2   Full penetration butt welds will be permitted in webs and flanges but not within 5.000m. of bridge centre line. Weld to be ground flush on bottom flanges and on exterior faces of webs on exterior beams. Direction of grinding to be transverse to direction of weld.
3   Elevation of all beams drawn to final beam profile
4   Bolt heads to be on outside face of external beams and on underside of all flanges
5   Shear studs to be set in rows parallel to stiffeners
6   Shear studs and tops of beams to be blast cleaned and primed only except for 20mm edge strips.

**TYPICAL DETAILS FOR A**
**3-SPAN CONTINUOUS COMPOSITE**
**CONSTRUCTION BRIDGE**

DRAWING NO. PGS 404/237A   SCALE : 1:10, 1:20, 1:50

DATE   APRIL 1977

SIR WILLIAM HALCROW & PARTNERS
CONSULTING ENGINEERS
SWINDON WILTS

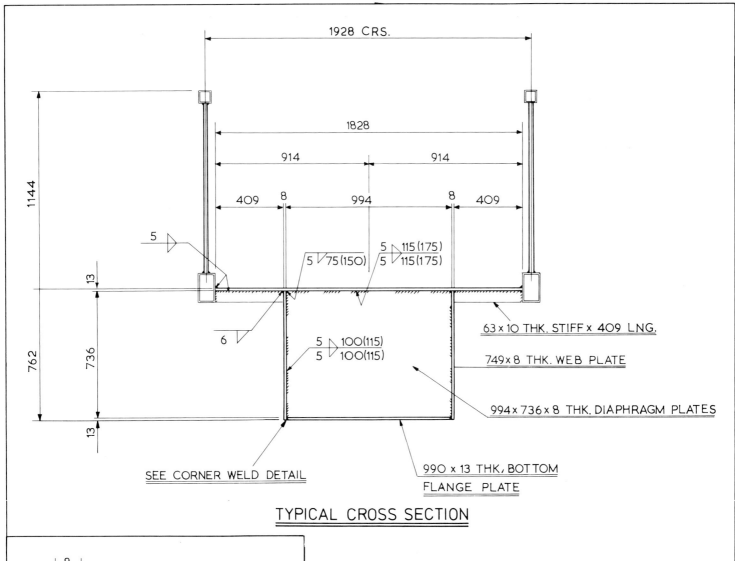

1928 CRS.

1828

914 914

409 8 994 8 409

1144

13

762 736

13

5

5 75(150)

5 115(175)
5 115(175)

6

5 100(115)
5 100(115)

63 x 10 THK. STIFF x 409 LNG.

749x 8 THK. WEB PLATE

994 x 736 x 8 THK. DIAPHRAGM PLATES

SEE CORNER WELD DETAIL

990 x 13 THK, BOTTOM
FLANGE PLATE

TYPICAL CROSS SECTION

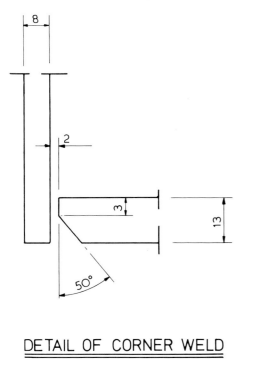

8

2

3

13

50°

DETAIL OF CORNER WELD

8.12 Cross section from a working drawing of a
footbridge designed and built by Adamson
Butterley Engineering Ltd. The footbridge
is made of welded plate using additional
rectangular hollow sections. Welds
specified to BS 499. (Supplied by Adamson
Butterley Engineering Ltd)

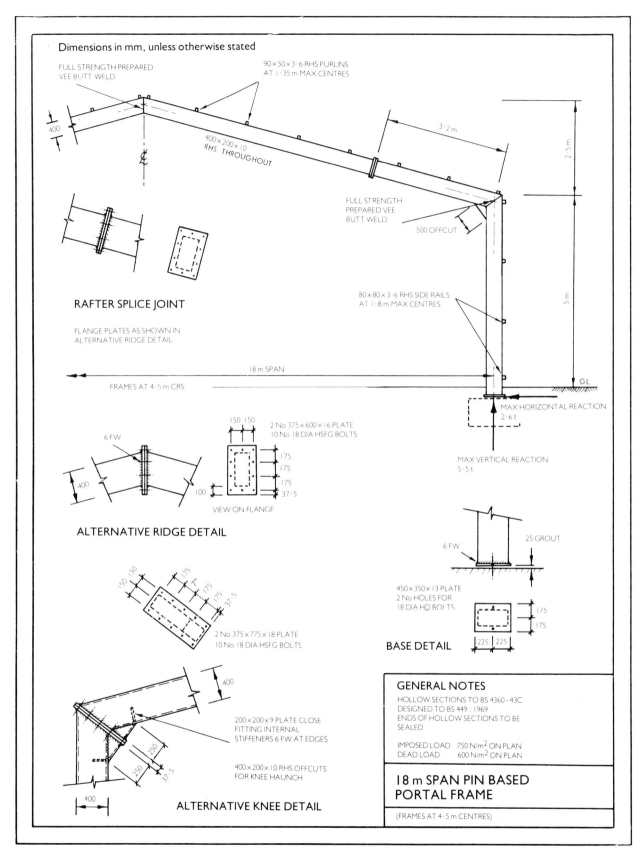

Dimensions in mm, unless otherwise stated

FULL STRENGTH PREPARED VEE BUTT WELD

90 × 50 × 3·6 RHS PURLINS AT 1·35 m MAX CENTRES

400

400 × 200 × 10 RHS THROUGHOUT

3·2 m

2·5 m

FULL STRENGTH PREPARED VEE BUTT WELD

500 OFFCUT

5 m

80 × 80 × 3·6 RHS SIDE RAILS AT 1·8 m MAX CENTRES

**RAFTER SPLICE JOINT**

FLANGE PLATES AS SHOWN IN ALTERNATIVE RIDGE DETAIL

18 m SPAN

FRAMES AT 4·5 m CRS

GL

MAX HORIZONTAL REACTION 2·6 t

MAX VERTICAL REACTION 5·5 t

6 FW

150  150

2 No 375 × 600 × 16 PLATE
10 No 18 DIA HSFG BOLTS

175
175
175
37·5

400

100

VIEW ON FLANGE

**ALTERNATIVE RIDGE DETAIL**

150  150    175  7"  175  37·5

2 No 375 × 775 × 18 PLATE
10 No 18 DIA HSFG BOLTS

25 GROUT

6 FW

450 × 350 × 13 PLATE
2 No HOLES FOR
18 DIA HD BOLTS

175
175

225  225

**BASE DETAIL**

400

200 × 200 × 9 PLATE CLOSE FITTING INTERNAL STIFFENERS 6 FW AT EDGES

250
250
37·5

400 × 200 × 10 RHS OFFCUTS FOR KNEE HAUNCH

400

**ALTERNATIVE KNEE DETAIL**

### GENERAL NOTES

HOLLOW SECTIONS TO BS 4360–43C
DESIGNED TO BS 449 : 1969
ENDS OF HOLLOW SECTIONS TO BE SEALED

IMPOSED LOAD   750 N/m² ON PLAN
DEAD LOAD       600 N/m² ON PLAN

## 18 m SPAN PIN BASED PORTAL FRAME

(FRAMES AT 4·5 m CENTRES)

8.13 *Elevation, section, and details of a pin-based portal frame suitable for a warehouse or workshop. The frame is of welded hollow section construction.*

*8.14 The map 1:2000 on the opposite page is made from a stereo pair of aerial photographs, one of which is shown here. The plot is made by* Photogrammetric Plotting System Wild Aviomap *with a servo-controlled plotting table and a computer-assisted drawing system directly scribed without any cartiographical working. (Photograph and plot supplied by Wild Heerbrugg Ltd)*

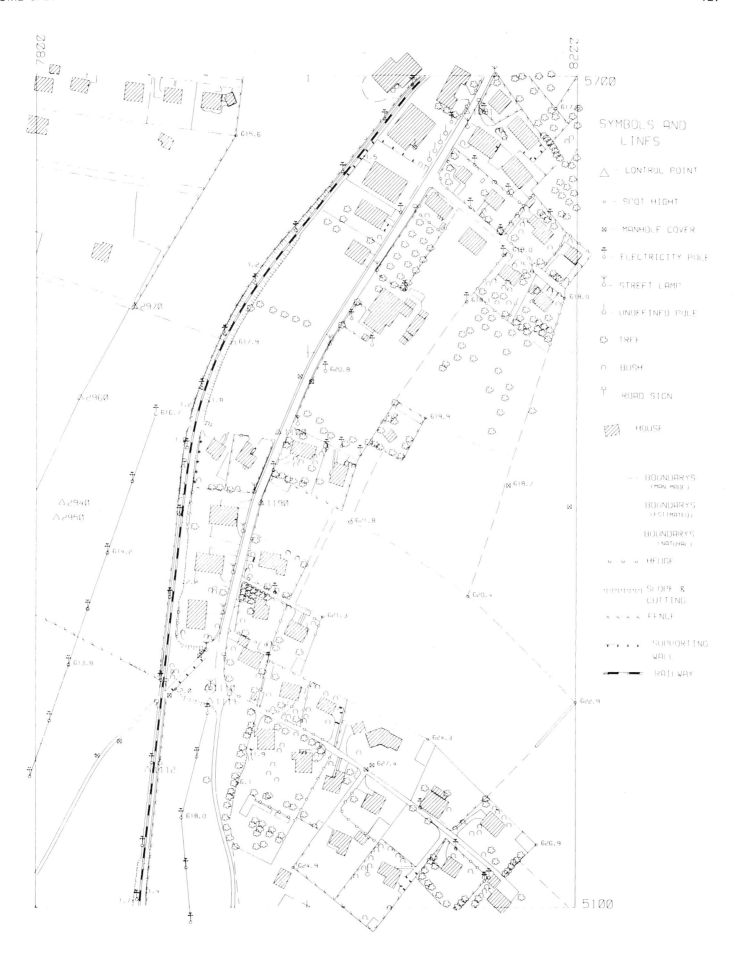

SYMBOLS AND
LINES

△ - CONTROL POINT

○ - SPOT HIGHT

⊠ - MANHOLE COVER

♯ - ELECTRICITY POLE

Υ - STREET LAMP

○ - UNDEFINED POLE

۞ - TREE

○ - BUSH

♀ - ROAD SIGN

▨ - HOUSE

--- BOUNDARYS
(MAN MADE)

BOUNDARYS
(ESTIMATED)

BOUNDARYS
(NATURAL)

○ ○ ○ HEDGE

↑↑↑↑↑ SLOPE &
CUTTING

× × × FENCE

· · · · SUPPORTING
WALL

▬▬▬ RAILWAY

The data collected in the field by the surveyor will provide information of:

(i) lengths

(ii) angles between fixed points

(iii) relative ground heights

and there are several methods by which combinations of these aspects are collected. They are:

(a) tape

(b) compass and tape (bearings and lengths)

(c) tacheometry – optical or electronic (angles, lengths, heights)

(d) levelling (heights)

(e) theodolite (angles)

(f) Electronic distance measurement (EDM) (lengths)

(g) photogrammetry (plan detail and relative heights).

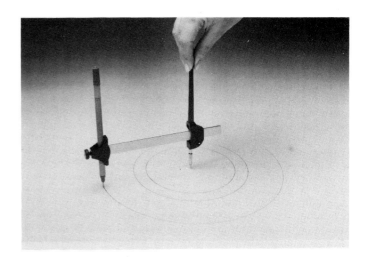

8.15 Beam compass. (Supplied by Blundell Harling Ltd)

8.16 Setting out angles.

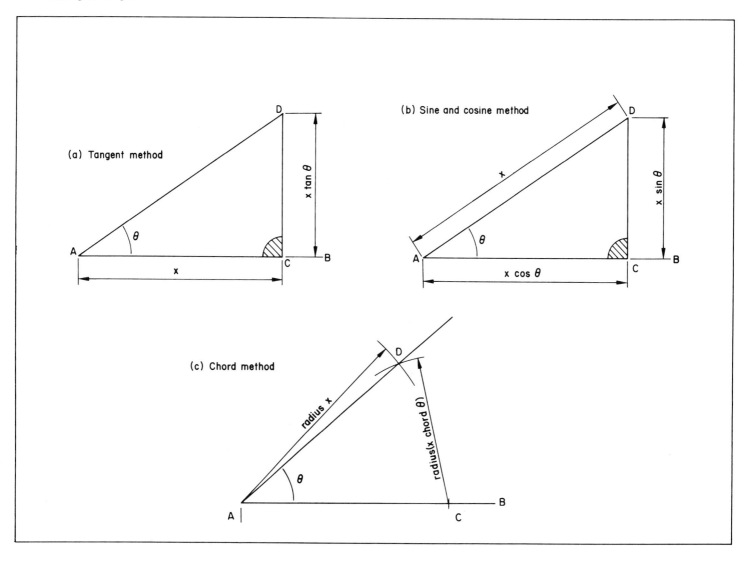

(a) Tangent method

(b) Sine and cosine method

(c) Chord method

**Tape**. At one time, this method would have been referred to as a chain survey, but steel tapes have now replaced, to a large extent, the traditional chain. The survey procedure and booking is, however, exactly the same.

Most reasonably level sites with good access can be surveyed by means of a tape and ranging rods only. The survey stations will then be related to each other by a system of triangles. The lengths of all the sides of the triangles will be known, but not the angles.

The stations are plotted by swinging arcs of radii equal to the sides of the triangles, using a beam compass (Fig. 8.15). The problem in this simple exercise is deciding upon the scale and locating the plotted survey neatly and symmetrically in the available space.

The only sure way, after having decided on the scale, is to plot the survey roughly in outline on a sheet of tracing paper. This can then be placed over the drawing paper and positioned so that it occupies the space neatly. Two station points can then be pricked through to the drawing paper and the survey plotted.

**Compass and tape traverse**. When the accuracy of the traverse is not too critical, i.e., when a plot is to be made from a site reconnaissance, then the compass will be good enough to provide basic information. Bearings measured by a compass are only accurate to about 5° and the plot is made using a 200 mm protractor. However, if the traverse line is long, an error at the edge of the protractor will be greatly magnified. In such cases more accurate methods of setting out should be used as shown in Fig. 8.16.

(a) Tangent method
   Locate C, x units from A
   Erect perpendicular at C
   Set off CD equal to x. tan $\theta$
   Join AD
(b) Sine and cosine method
   Locate C, x. cos $\theta$ units from A
   Erect perpendicular at C
   Set off CD equal to x. sin $\theta$
   Join AD which should then be x units long.
(c) Chord method
   Locate C, x units from A
   Swing arc centre A radius x units
   Centre C, swing an arc radius x times the chord of angle $\theta$. Join AD

Method (c) is the quickest and most accurate method if a table of chords is available. Of course, the acute angles between the traverse lines at the survey stations should be used for greater accuracy and convenience.

**Tacheometry**. Areas of ground and the collection of topographical detail can be accomplished quickly using tacheometry. From the field bookings, having used a theodolite and levelling staff, information can be gathered with reasonable speed. The computation of the data collected is a little more laborious. Accuracy is not very high and the plotting of the bearings is done by a protractor, as before.

As the plotting of a tacheometric survey requires numerous radial lines to be drawn, these should be done very feintly as they may have to be erased at the completion of the work.

Greater speed and accuracy can be obtained using a tacheometer capable of automatically recording field observations.

**Levelling**. There are occasions when the relative heights of the ground have to be plotted, i.e., for the location of contours. If a piece of ground has been surveyed in order that contours may be established, it is most probable that the surveyor will have laid out a grid over the whole area and then determined the heights of the points relative to an Ordnance Survey Bench Mark or a Temporary Bench Mark established near the site.

It will be necessary to plot the grid on the paper and enter the levels, reduced to datum, to enable the contours to be drawn. The grid and figuring may have to be erased later so they are drawn feintly.

As most of the spot levels taken at the grid points will not correspond with the actual level of a contour, see Fig. 8.17, the positions of the contour on the grid lines will have to be found

by interpolation. In some instances this can be done by 'eye', but if a more accurate position is required, an inerpolation graph could be used, see Fig. 8.18 and Fig. 8.19.

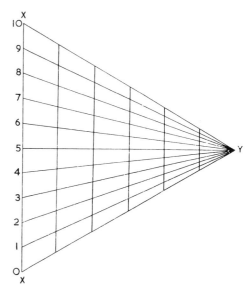

8.18 Interpolation graph.

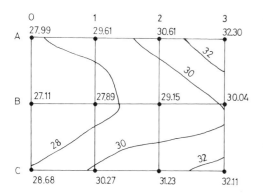

8.17 Contours on grid.

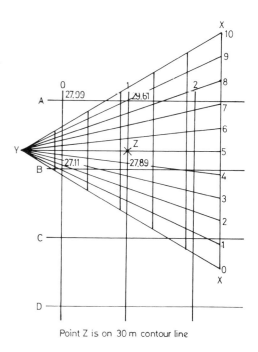

Point Z is on 30 m contour line

8.19 Interpolation graph on grid.

**Theodolite**. Survey stations which have been located very accurately by triangulation using a theodolite, steel tape, EDM or other means of determining the precise distances, are plotted, after the data obtained in the field have been computated, to obtain the co-ordinates of the stations as Eastings or Northings. The calculated co-ordinates will be relative to a pair of arbitrarily chosen axes at right angles and will be set out with reference to a grid which will have been plotted with meticulous care and accuracy, see Fig. 8.20.

The grid must not be constructed by means of a parallel rule and set square as this can lead to inaccuracy. It is plotted by the geometrical construction of right angles so:

(a) Draw any convenient line AB with a straight edge.

(b) Select point C at the left-hand end of the line AB. Erect a perpendicular through C by choosing any point O and with radius OC swing an arc to cut the given line at P. It is advisable to make the radius OC as large as possible. Produce PO to meet the other side of the arc Q, thereby drawing the diameter POQ. Join CQ which is then perpendicular to the given line.

(c) Set off along CD and CF a convenient multiple of grid units.

(d) Centre D, radius CF, swing an arc DE.

(e) Centre F, radius CD, swing an arc to cut the previous arc at E.

(f) Divide CD, FE, CF and DE into grid units (100 mm, 200 mm, etc.) as shown in Fig.

8.20, and join the points with a straight edge, thus completing the grid. The grid may sometimes be finished in ink, using feint lines.

Survey stations are located from the nearest grid line, not from the axes.

**Electronic distance measurement (EDM)**. A great deal of time can be saved in field surveys using EDM equipment. At one period, these instruments were combined with a conventional theodolite and a pulse of light was emitted and then reflected back to the instrument from a reflector sited at the point to be measured. The data obtained needed a fair amount of computing before the results could be presented for plotting. Now the instruments

*8.20 Construction of a grid.*

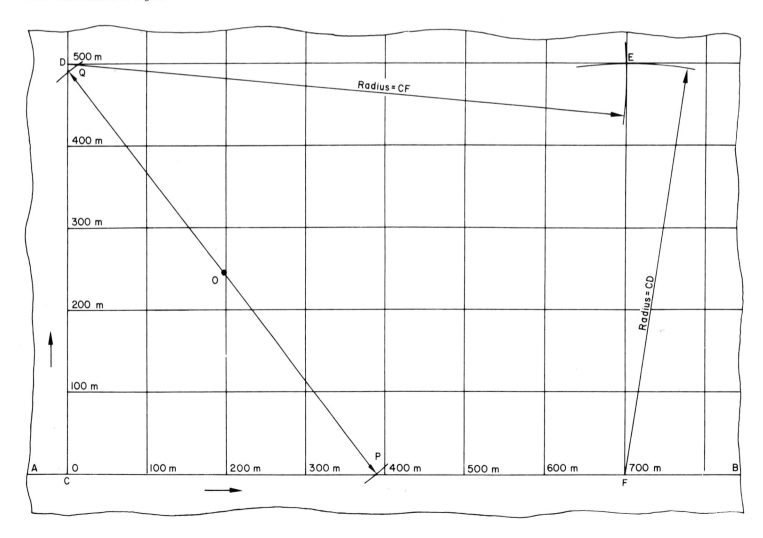

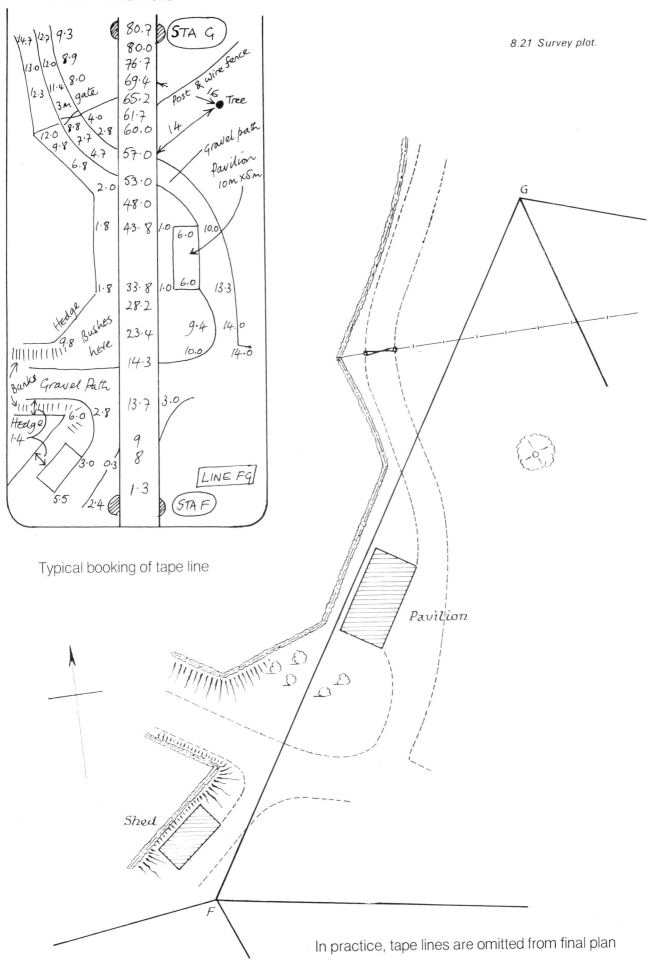

Typical booking of tape line

8.21 Survey plot.

In practice, tape lines are omitted from final plan

use low power laser or more commonly now, an infra-red beam giving an instant digital read-out of length, slope, distances and angles. The data have still to be plotted as will be seen in Chapter 10, this can now be fully digitised and fed into an automatic plotter.

**Photogrammetry**. As has been seen in Fig. 8.14, surveying can be carried out by means of stereo pairs of aerial photographs or by means of land-based cameras taking stereo pairs of photographs. Special pieces of apparatus are used by which means topographical detail and contours can be obtained from the photographic pairs. Photogrammetry still requires a certain amount of land surveying to be done to establish such things as control points and these have to be located accurately before the other detail can be added at the plotting table.

### (d) Filling in topographical detail

By whatever method the traverse has been surveyed and plotted, most of the topographical detail will be located by simple, offset measurements from the traverse lines. Most offset measurements will be made at right angles to the traverse lines, although there are exceptions when, for example, a tree or corner of a building is positioned. This can be seen in Fig. 8.21, which shows a page from a field book on which offsets and distances along the tape are recorded together with a plot of the same detail. Note that this particular example has been recorded in metres.

An offset scale speeds plotting, see Fig. 8.22. It is a short scale, fully divided to its square ends, which can slide along a full size scale held in place on the traverse line by weights.

Common conventions are used in plotting surveys and some of them are shown in Fig. 8.23. Other conventions can be found in the margins of *Ordnance Survey* maps.

Surveys must indicate the North, whether it be magnetic, grid or True. The north symbol should be simply drawn as in the examples in Fig. 8.24, and north should normally be at the top of the sheet or towards the right-hand side.

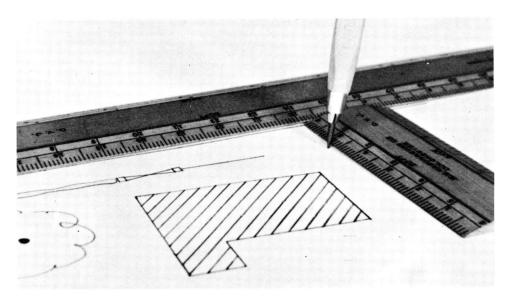

*8.22 Offset scale.*

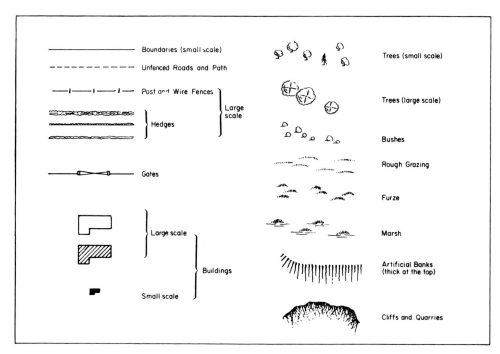

*8.23 Conventions.*

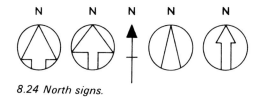

*8.24 North signs.*

# Chapter 9

# The drawing office and the reproduction of drawings

*Engineering on a small scale: Kingsgate foot-bridge at Durham. To save erecting scaffolding in the river, the symmetrical halves of the bridge were built parallel to the banks and, on completion, were swung out to meet each other. The engineer was given a very free brief for this bridge and devised this novel, but very elegant and economical, solution. (Photograph supplied by the engineer, Mr Ove Arup of Ove Arup & Partners)*

## 9.1 INTRODUCTION

In many establishments, the distinction between the design office and the drawing office is becoming less and less. Finished drawings are now being prepared by graduate engineers, and undergraduates on a sandwich degree course, working in the design office. It is considered necessary that graduates can produce drawings in order to be able to 'lead by example' in a design team.

The number of skilled draughtsmen and tracers is steadily dwindling and a large number of them have now turned free-lance, firms using them as and when the demands of work require their services. It is very expensive to use free-lancers but more economical than employing a draughtsman or tracer full-time, when the work load is intermittent.

Many engineers start their professional lives as part of a design team, spending a good deal of time at the drawing board, if not actually in a drawing office.

At one time, engineering drawings were made on cartridge paper from which an ink tracing on linen was made. Copies were then taken on a paper base called blue-print. In due course this method of copying drawings was replaced by a semipermanent photographic process known as dyeline.

Drawings are now made on tracing paper which frequently has the title box and border pre-printed on the sheets. Sizes of paper are also frequently standardised for the work of a particular firm.

The sheer bulk of full size drawings, tracings and prints creates storage problems. The solution is to microfilm everything on to 35 mm or 16 mm photographic slides, mounted in an aperture in a standard size computer card. Enlargements can be easily made from the microfilm by means of a process camera.

A considerable amount of design and survey information is now stored on disc files for use in a mini-computer. The information can be displayed as required on a Visual Display Unit (VDU) and appropriate parts of the drawing can then be printed out for use on site, etc.

This chapter is concerned with the routine side of drawing office work and is an introduction to referencing, filing and the storage of drawings and methods of reproducing them. The subject is only dealt with in a general way as the permutations of drawing office management are beyond the scope of the book.

## 9.2 PLAN REFERENCES

It is essential that every sketch, drawing or schedule must have a reference number which is individual to that piece of paper. The manner in which this referencing is done, will vary from firm to firm.

Smaller firms, for example, may simply number each drawing as it is produced, irrespective of the scheme to which it belongs. On the other hand, they may follow the practice of larger organisations, by which each scheme has a job number and all drawings, etc., for that scheme are numbered consecutively under that reference.

Any system that is used will have to ensure that two drawings are not issued with the same number. A single register, with the drawing numbers already written in, could be used in a smaller organisation. It is surprising how many errors can occur if each person who registers a drawing has to write down a number following on consecutively from the one above. A minimum of information, the title of the drawing, its size, the date of registration and possibly the person who prepared it, is entered against each number.

If more information is required, as in the case of a large organisation, either a card index system or a drawing register for each job number, can be used.

In the latter case, additional information such as details of amendments, print issues, date of microfilming, whether drawing has been destroyed or perhaps returned to the client at the end of the job, can all be entered on the card index or register.

An organisation must decide how much information it needs to record and how it is going to keep the records up to date. This is very important in the case of revisions or amendments to drawings. It is equally important that the system includes a register of all those persons who have received prints, in order that they can be sent a revised issue. It is their responsibility to destroy earlier prints. Sometimes revised prints are sent to one person, perhaps the architect for the scheme, for him to make the print distribution. This question of revised issues is very important and frequently overlooked by a busy office. Disaster could occur if the site engineer found himself working to an out-of-date print.

Usually drawings have a block in the lower right-hand corner in which details of each amendment are written, the date carried out and a prefix added to the drawing number, A, B, C, etc., denoting a revision.

In the case of bar schedules for reinforced concrete details, these too must be referenced not only to the job but also to the drawing to which they refer.

## 9.3 STORAGE

A drawing or design office may have at least four different types of material to store, each of which must be so filed that they are easily recoverable for reference, printing, etc. They are:

(a) drawings
(b) schedules
(c) microfilms
(d) correspondence, design sheets, etc.

Even if at a later date, drawings are microfilmed, destroyed or returned to the client, some storage will be needed for them whilst the job is in hand.

Large organisations in particular, tend to use drawing media of standard sizes only – A0, B0, A1 etc., and these are frequently pre-printed with the firm's name, a title block and a border on each sheet. Such standardisation assists considerably when it comes to the question of storage.

Drawings may be stored, or filed, horizontally in drawers, or in one of the vertical filing systems.

Drawers more than 50 mm deep, become very heavy when full, while replacing drawings in a full drawer or filing a flimsy tracing is almost impossible, with or without help.

Horizontal storage chests, see Fig. 9.1, require at least twice their own floor area for convenient operation. The flat top of the chest is however, very useful for holding drawings either after their removal or before filing them.

Vertical storage systems occupy less floor space than horizontal chests for similar storage capacity and they need considerably less floor space in operation, see Fig. 9.2. They lack of course, the facility for spreading drawings out as mentioned previously.

The location, accessibility of drawings and ingenious methods to prevent smaller drawings from slipping to the bottom of the cabinet, are the main differences in the various vertical filing systems that have been divised. All must, however, have some method by which drawings are gripped to enable them to be suspended in the cabinet. Small or odd-sized drawings upset most systems and it is for this reason consideation is given to the standardisation of drawing sizes.

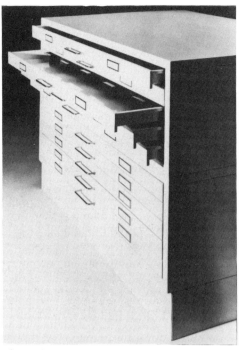

9.1 Horizontal storage cabinet. (Supplied by Utopia Drawing Office Equipment Ltd)

Schedules, correspondence and design sheets, will store more readily in three- or four-drawer steel filing cabinets. The drawers can contain racks for holding suspended files which are readily indexed for rapid and easy access.

9.2 Vertical storage cabinet. (Supplied by Utopia Drawing Office Equipment Ltd)

Microfilms, see section 9.5, cut and mounted in aperture cards are easily stored in small drawers or boxes, depending upon the quantity involved. Each card must carry the reference number of the drawing involved. The cards are either indexed for hand sorting, or punched for automatic sorting.

For security purposes a microfilm reel can be stored in a separate location, in addition to the production of aperture cards.

Correspondence tends to accumulate to enormous proportions throughout the period of a job. This can be accommodated very easily on 16 mm microfilm, the original material being subsequently destroyed.

## 9.4 REPRODUCING DRAWINGS

There are two main methods in use for reproducing engineering drawings, the dyeline process and the electrographic process. The dyeline process produces a black line from a black line in the original, unlike the normal photographic process where an intermediate, negative stage is introduced, and these prints are cheaper than any other form of reproduction.

The electrographic or electrostatic process can be set up to make black line prints from positive or negative originals.

In the dyeline process, a sensitised coating on the paper is developed, after exposure to light, to produce a dark line of dye where there was a line on the original. Development is either dry, by ammonia gas or semidry, when the coated surface is dampened with a minimum of developing solution that soon soaks into the paper and evaporates. This image is not fixed in the photographic sense and can deteriorate if continuously exposed to daylight. Exposure and developing are done in the same machine in the majority of cases, see Fig. 9.3.

Originally dyeline prints were always made the same size as the original by exposing the paper to light through the tracing which was in contact with it. Prints can now be made by projection from microfilm positives on to dyeline paper, thus making possible almost any degree of enlargement or reduction from the original size.

In addition to the rotary type of dyeline printer there is a True-to-Scale flatbed version for reproducing prints accurately, as the name implies.

Reproductions can be made without microfilming by photographing the original to the size required with very large cameras and making a positive transparency for dyeline printing from the negative. A positive is necessary for each degree of reduction.

In the electrophotographic process, an image of the original is projected on to an electrostatically charged photoconductive material. The action of light causes the electrostatic

9.3 Dyeline printer. (Supplied by Ozalid (UK) Ltd)

charge to leak away leaving lines of charge in place of black lines on the original. A reversal of the charge makes it possible to reverse the image and print directly from the negative image obtained in the microfilm camera.

The photoconductive material can be part of the machine, often a selenium-coated drum, or a coated paper with a conductive base.

Fine carbon particles, attracted by the electrostatic charge, are transferred from the drum to the printing paper and are fixed by heat fusion, or they are attracted directly to the conductive based paper and then fused. If the fusion is complete, the image is virtually permanent, otherwise the carbon dust rubs off almost at once.

Before the advent of polyester film, all tracings were made on specially treated fine linen. The linen is either dyed blue or left white, neither leaves any background on the print, as dyeline paper does not react to blue light. For this reason, blue pencil lines, used to lay out a drawing, need not be erased.

Today, most drawings are made directly on to polyester film or tracing paper from which good prints can be made of pencil work. Some offices ink in dimensions or background material for greater clarity.

The dyeline process can produce copies on four different media:

(a) ordinary paper
(b) tracing paper
(c) polyester film
(d) linen.

## 9.5 MICROFILM SYSTEMS

An ever increasing number of drawing and design offices utilise microfilm systems. The decision to set up a microfilm section is usually taken when the volume of drawings and dyeline printout copies reaches such proportions that filing and storage pose problems. Expenditure on the additional equipment required, a planetary camera, a film processing machine, a printout machine and reading equipment is justified by the enormous benefits that a microfilm service provides. These are:

(a) A considerable saving in space.
(b) Time saved by greater ease and speed of access.
(c) Ease of duplication by a cheap process.
(d) The safe retention of the master drawings which are then never allowed outside the office.
(e) Postal despatch of film copies of draw-

ings is easy and cheap, so that branches of a company can have up-to-date drawings.

The standard film size for engineering drawings is 35 mm, and silver halide film is used because of its tested archival quality, but copies issued for use can well be on diazo film which is cheaper. All the film stock used is

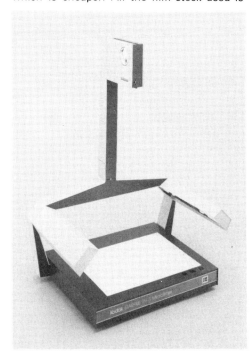

9.4 Planetary camera – Kodak 'Starfile' RV–3 Microfilmer. (Supplied by Kodak Ltd)

9.6 Microform reader. (Supplied by 3M United Kingdom Ltd)

safety film, that is to say it is difficult to ignite and slow in burning.

The drawings are filmed by a planetary camera, see Fig. 9.4, and the film cut and mounted in an aperture card which is a standard size computer card with an opening to carry the 35 mm piece of film, this could on occasions be 16 mm, see Fig. 9.5. The film part of the card can be viewed on a microform

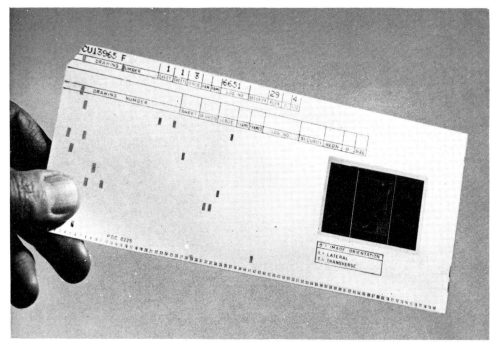

9.5 An aperture card.

*9.7  Microfilm process camera. (Supplied by 3M, United Kingdom Ltd)*

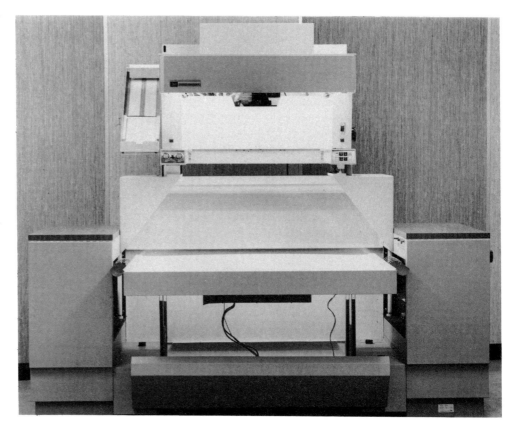

reader, see Fig. 9.6. Some readers can also make copies of the slide, whilst enlarged copies of the drawing can be made by a process camera, see Fig. 9.7.

Once an office is committed to a microform system, it is essential that new drawings are made according to the recommendations contained in BS 5444: *Recommendations for Preparation of Copy for Microcopying*, and BS 4210: *35 mm Microcopying of Technical Drawings*. These deal with such matters as the thickness of the lines in drawing, sizes of letters to be used, etc., for a drawing reproduced from a film cannot be better than the original drawing. Modern printout machines produce a positive or negative output, that is black on white or white on black, at the touch of a switch, Fig. 9.8.

Although printouts are readily made from the filmed drawing, quite a lot of use will be made of the film without recourse to the printouts, the drawing being projected from the film either on to the desk, the wall or the screen of the microfilm reader, depending on the equipment in use. Thus an engineer can refer to any drawing he requires without having to search through vast quantities of paper.

Much time can be spent in collecting drawings from the central filing system, chasing up the ones already out, and refiling them after use. Offices overcome this problem by issuing non-returnable diazo microfilm copies, each user having a microfilm reader. The cost of the system is covered by the saving in time. The central store of microfilm negatives is easily kept up to date and full-sized copies can be produced as required, but normal use is by viewing on the screen of a microfilm reader. A very rapid service results.

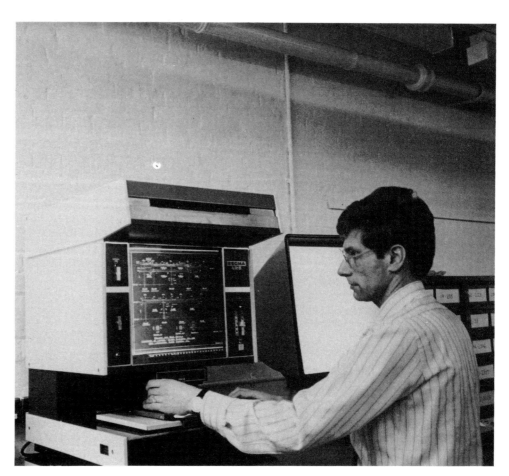

*9.8  Microfilm reader and printer. (Supplied by R. Travers Morgan, Consulting Engineers, London)*

# Chapter 10    Computers and drawing

Engineering on a large scale: Mangla Dam, West Pakistan. This is part of the colossal Indus Basin Scheme, and is the result of international cooperation on the grand scale. It was needed because of the re-arrangment of the Punjab irrigation system after Pakistan was separated from India. Part of the cost was met by the World Bank; the Dam was de-signed by British engineers with American associates, and it was built by a consortium of American contractors. The photograph is of the spillway which can drop about 28 000 cubic metres of water a second about 100 m. (Photograph supplied by Binnie and Partners who were the consulting engineers)

## 10.1 INTRODUCTION

The computer in the design and drawing office, with the associated equipment, can be used in two ways.:

(a) to generate graphic information
(b) to plot graphic information from given data.

## 10.2 GENERATION OF GRAPHIC INFORMATION

The computer's great speed and infallible memory complement man's intuition if a quick, two-way method of communication is available. The method of communication by punched tape, card, magnetic tape or disc input, which the machine can read at great speed but which man can prepare only relatively slowly, is not economical in time or money.

A graphical output is more readily assimilated than is a line printout and this led to the development of a system in which man and the machine communicate by means of a visual display on a cathode ray tube. Starting with an empty screen, an operator draws lines on the cathode ray tube by means of a light pencil, thereby leaving a trace on the screen. The system is able to straighten out wavy lines or draw vertical or horizontal ones as instructed and rotate diagonal ones until they fit. The ends of lines meeting at angles can be made to join.

Once a pattern is completed, an instruction from the keyboard will send the picture to the computer's memory store and wipe it off the screen whilst other draughting takes place. The information can be recalled at any time, at any size and adjusted, if necessary, for location and orientation, see Fig. 10.1.

The light pencil has now been superseded, to some extent, in civil engineering work by other means, although the principles involved are very similar. Some ways in which graphical information can be produced are:

(a) by digital data obtained from co-ordinates together with operating orders read in from the data medium;
(b) by a graphics unit and VDU;
(c) by an electronic lettering and drawing system.

The last two decades have witnessed great strides in the application of computer solutions to problems in civil engineering work generally. The usefulness of a computer system, however, is too often limited by the restrictions of its human interface – the methods of allowing people to enter and access information. Interactive techniques such as the use of on-line terminals, make computers approachable and responsive.

But for many applications, conventional input–output terminals present the user with a mass of alphanumeric data that must be interpreted. What is required by the user, is a format that conveys information visually and effectively. Computer graphics does just that, giving a complete picture like nothing else can.

Until recently, using computer graphics had been costly, but with the advancement of micro-chip techniques the situation has changed dramatically. So much so, that almost each day new applications of the technology make yesterday's equipment out of date. It is necessary, when looking at graphics to look at the complete picture, look at todays application, look at tomorrows opportunities.

Until the advent of ultra-modern micro-electronics it was necessary to draw everything afresh. There are now available electronic drawing systems using a normal typewriter keyboard plus some function keys, symbols and text that is stored and called up as required; the result being a new perspective to drawing and lettering. By adding an external tape-cassette memory, programmes entered in the working memory can be recorded and called up according to need.

The system (a) is further extended in the collection of survey field data by means of an electronic tacheometer which can either record digital information from survey observations direct on to magnetic tape, or via a recording

10.1 Light pencil. (Supplied by Aristo Graphic System)

10.2 Electronic tacheometer and field book. (Supplied by Kern & Co. Ltd, Switzerland)

10.3   Digitiser unit.

field book or by a digitiser, see Fig. 10.2 and Fig. 10.3. All the information, from whatever source, can then be fed into a desk top computer.

System (b) can be found in two operational modes.

(i) Graphics are generated on a screen by means of a microprocessor input – in some ways comparable to the input by an electronic pencil.

(ii) By using a digitiser to obtain co-ordinates which when fed into the VDU can produce either an alphanumeric display or give graphical information, see Fig. 10.4.

The third system (c) uses a perfectly normal typewriter keyboard plus a few function keys. Drawing and lettering are rationalised to such an extent that more time is available for other tasks. The machine is in the form of a frame that can be placed on paper of any working size, the working area is thus virtually unlimited from the size of a postage stamp to the size of a large poster, see Fig. 10.5.

10.4   The graphic work station of the WILD INFORMAP system for digitising exist-ing plans, for editing plans before automatic plotting, for checking, up-dating and managing the data base, and for producing data extracts.

   Information previously entered into the data base can be called up selectively from the computer storage and displayed on the graphic screen.

   The digital map is continuously con-verted into a drawing on the graphic screen and plans and maps can be enlarged or reduced at will. (Supplied by Wild Heerbrugg Ltd)

On the simpler side, if orthographic projections of an object are drawn, the systems described under (a) and (b) can be programmed to recreate orthographic, isometric or perspective images from its stored three-dimensional data.

Isometric drawings, see Fig. 10.7, of very complicated pipework in three dimensions, such as would be used in oil refineries or the chemical industry, can be drawn by these systems using a large range of symbols for valves, junctions, tapers, etc., in the computer store.

A civil engineering application is the design and drawing of a system building which can be made to fit any dimensions given by a customer. In this case, a store of a thousand or so standard items can be called upon to provide structural details. In addition, an outline of the building can be called up. Any number of the single-storey units can be fitted together, sides moved in or out and the roof raised or lowered to fit the required specification. The computer can then analyse the structure to specified loadings so that the components of the proper size can be used to prepare the drawings, see Fig. 10.8.

System (b) comprises basically a central processing unit in which are stored all the graphic symbols, lines, lettering, etc. These are drawn, as required, by a graphics draughting unit, Fig. 10.6, which assembles what is taken from

*10.5   Electronic draughting and lettering. (Supplied by Albeta Ltd)*

the CPU store into a meaningful drawing, according to the requirements of the designer. When completed, the whole graphic illustration can be stored back in the CPU and access to the information obtained as required. There is an additional peripheral in the form of a visual display unit for alphanumeric symbols.

## 10.3   PLOTTING THE GRAPHIC INFORMATION

Having obtained and stored the graphic information, it can either be accessed and displayed on a VDU or it can be fed into an automatic plotter which will present the information in a permanent form as a drawing.

There are two main forms of plotter, drum and flat bed. Both use some style of pen and ink for producing the graphic work and these can lead to some problems with ink flow. The drum plotter, see Fig. 10.9, is generally a slower process than the flat bed using the same drawing instrument. Recent developments now use the electrostatic process of reproduction by the drum plotter and this has speeded up this system way beyond that of the others. There is no drying up of the ink and the result can be regulated, within limits, to provide copy of any density. One system can produce a highly complicated A1 size drawing

*10.6   Graphics draughting unit. (Supplied by Kern & Co. Ltd, Switzerland)*

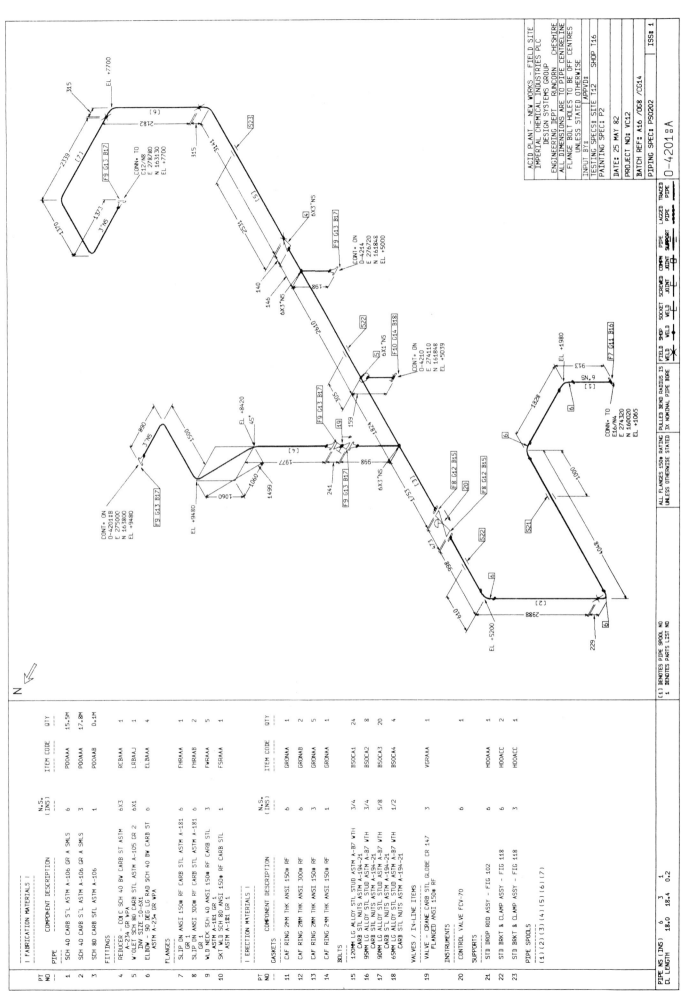

10.7 Isometric piping drawing. (Supplied by ICI Ltd)

10.8  *The figure shows a typical example of a civil engineering building plan. The module units drawn by an automatic draughting machine from sub-routine tapes and inserted at the desired co-ordinates, have been produced on tape by conventional digitising techniques. The times taken to complete the plans were as shown. (Supplied by F.C.S. Controls Ltd)*

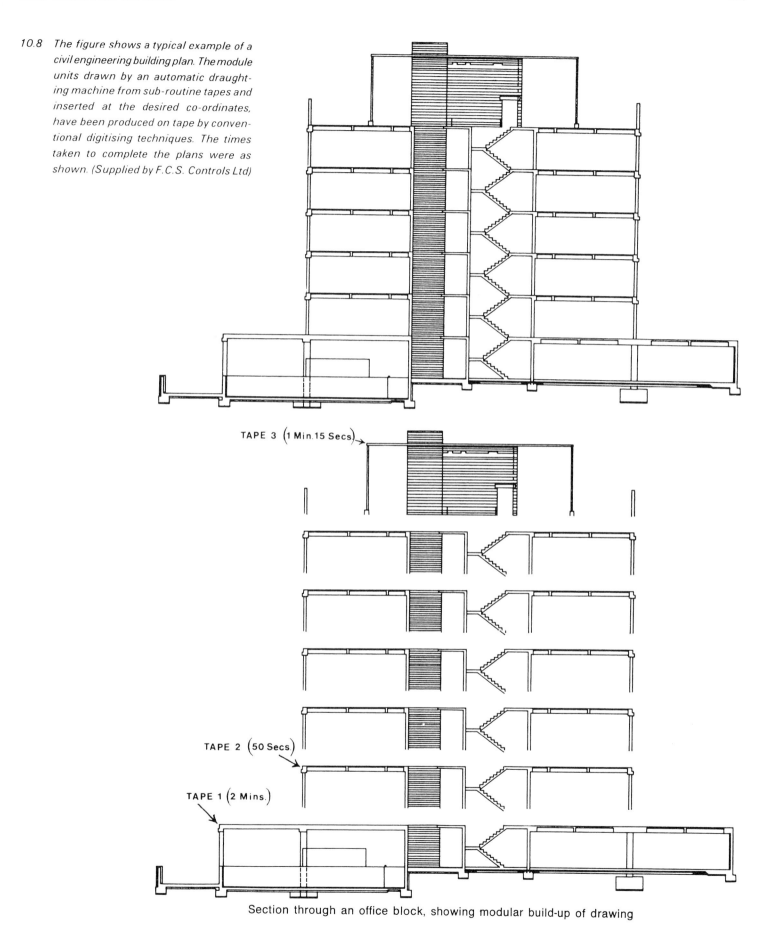

TAPE 3 (1 Min.15 Secs.)

TAPE 2 (50 Secs.)

TAPE 1 (2 Mins.)

Section through an office block, showing modular build-up of drawing

10.10 Benson model 1425 flat-bed plotter with
(Supplied by Benson Electronics Ltd)

in about two minutes. Like other drum plotters, the mechanism operates in the x axis, the rotation of the drum providing the y axis.

There are many varieties of the flat-bed plotter, see Fig. 10.10, or, as it is sometimes referred to, the graphic peripheral. The basic operation is for a pen to traverse along an arm or beam in the y axis, whilst the beam itself travels along the x axis. Pens of various size or with different coloured inks are incorporated in the drawing head. Automatic plotters are in effect, high precision draughting machines, but almost twenty times more accurate than the conventional manual design.

To maintain accuracy, the drawing surface must be very flat and for this reason optically flat ground glass is usually used. It also has the advantage that it can be illuminated from below.

A table plotter can accept any drawing medium of any size up to its maximum capacity.

10.10 Benson model 1425 flatbed plotter with
integral screen and keyboard. (Supplied
by Benson Electronics Ltd)

A drum plotter on the other hand, is limited only by the length of its roll of paper.

Plotters are slow compared with computers and so are operated off-line, i.e. by a paper or magnetic tape or by disc output from the computer, which can then go on to other work.

The plotter can be used to draw road cross sections and alignments from design and survey data, see Fig. 10.11. In the same way, an optimum route can be determined giving a balance of cut and fill that is most economical. It can generate isometric views or perspectives as easily as it can an orthographic view, see Fig. 10.12.

## 10.4 INERACTIVE COMPUTER GRAPHICS

New or revised construction works, i.e., roads, buildings, the laying of gas and other services, are constantly taking place and to maintain up-to-date information on all existing maps and plans would be an almost impossible task.

If a large undertaking has to prepare a new project, it would be necessary to make reference to a whole series of relevant plans, taken from a wide range of sources. It is more than likely that these reference plans would themselves be out of date.

New concepts to the solution of this problem have been devised in which computer graphics play an important role. They are referred to as 'Interactive graphics, mapping and data base systems'. One such system, and described here, is INFORMAP WILDMAR as marketed by Wild Heerbrugg Ltd of Switzerland.

The system allows firms, planning authorities, public utilities, surveyors and technical administrators to keep the flow of information and data under control, so that results are achieved on time and economically. The logical and consistent integration of photogrammetric plotting instruments, the results from electro-tacheometric surveys, a mini-computer with a large storage capacity, a data-base program system, interactive computer graphics and automatic plotting equipment, create the best possible conditions for the largely automated production of plans and maps. Diagramatically the system is as shown in Fig. 10.13.

The performance of an interactive graphic system is influenced decisively by the organisation and structure of the data-base software. It must provide universal and rapid access and efficient data management.

It can be divided into three organisational levels as shown in Fig. 10.14.

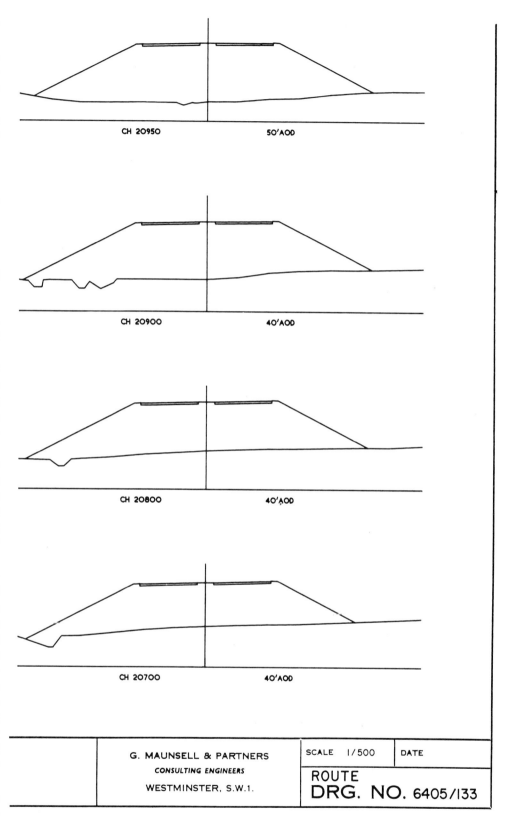

CH 20950          50'AOD

CH 20900          40'AOD

CH 20800          40'AOD

CH 20700          40'AOD

| G. MAUNSELL & PARTNERS | SCALE 1/500 | DATE |
| CONSULTING ENGINEERS | ROUTE | |
| WESTMINSTER, S.W.1. | DRG. NO. 6405/133 | |

*10.11 Motorway cross sections. (Supplied by G. Maunsell & Partners)*

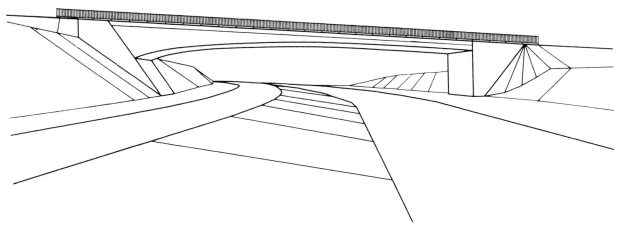

## PERSPECTIVE DRAWING

*10.12 Perspective view of bridge over a motorway.*

*10.13 Automation chain from data acquisition to data output.*

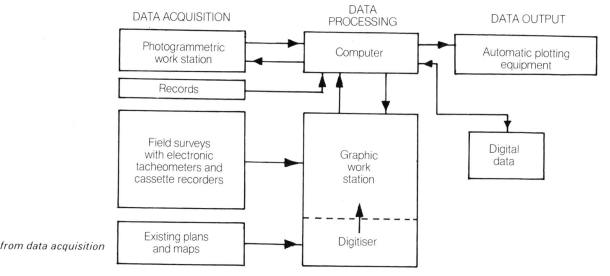

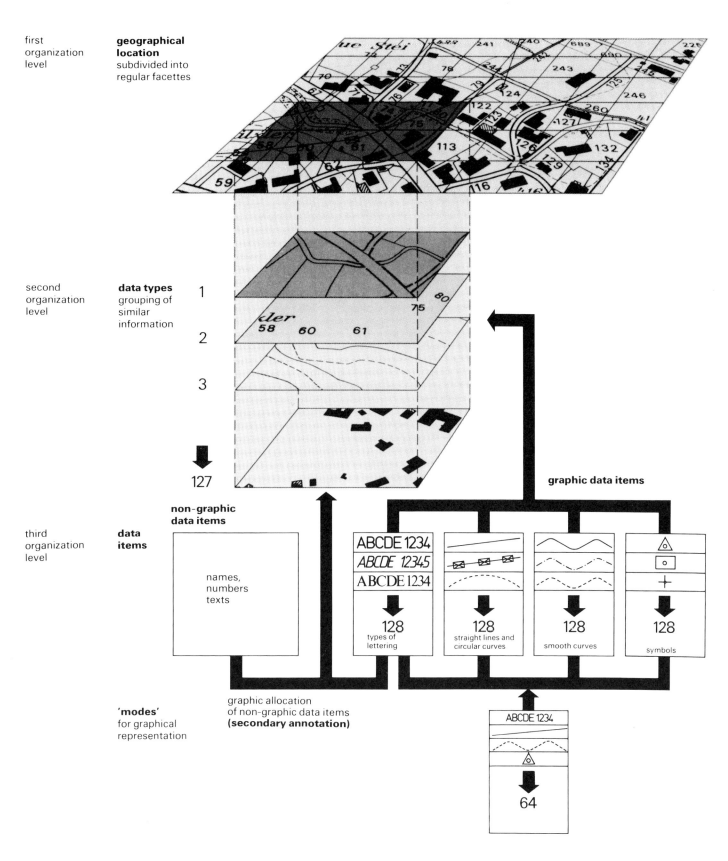

first
organization
level

**geographical
location**
subdivided into
regular facettes

second
organization
level

**data types**
grouping of
similar
information

1

2

3

127

non-graphic
data items

**data
items**

names,
numbers
texts

third
organization
level

**graphic data items**

ABCDE 1234
*ABCDE 12345*
ABCDE 1234

128
types of
lettering

128
straight lines and
circular curves

128
smooth curves

128
symbols

'modes'
for graphical
representation

graphic allocation
of non-graphic data items
**(secondary annotation)**

ABCDE 1234

64

10.14 WILD data base. (Supplied by Wild
Heerbrugg, Switzerland)

## (a) First level – geographical location

Sub-divided into regular shapes, called facettes. All the data within a facette are placed in a separate file (computer). This makes possible direct access to the data of a facette, without the need to search all the data of the entire area in question.

## (b) Second level – data types

Groups of similar information. Within each facette, the data are divided into different data types – 127 in the WILDMAP system. This gives the user direct and rapid access to special categories of data within a facette.

## (c) Third level – data items

These are sub-divided into non-graphic and graphic items.

**Non-graphic items.** Here are stored texts and lists, such as names of streets, owners and information on public utilities such as diameters, depths, year of construction, etc.

**Graphic items.** These specify the graphical representation of a data type. They are sub-divided into a number of classes: straight lines, circular curves, smooth curves, types of lettering and linework, symbols, etc.

**Variable mapping of data items.** Data base software is designed such that data items are stored independently of the scale representation. Each data item can be stored in many modes, (up to 64 in the WILD system). Storing up to 128 symbols in 64 ways means that 8192 symbols can be plotted.

**Allocation of items.** Non-graphic data items are allocated to graphic items and are automatically marked on the plan.

For data-based management, the system provides for the automatic establishment of lists and/or the graphical representation of accurately defined connections, such as occur particularly in statistical analysis, the renewal of public utilities in planning tasks and for cadastral and rating purposes.

This means that the user can, at any time, have the required map prepared precisely, based on any desired combination of data and of any area, regardless of map sheets already available to existing sheet boundaries.

# Index